Dear Readers . . .

In 1981, "The People's Friend" introduced a new feature to the magazine called "The Farmer And His Wife". It was a series of country tales told by fictional farmer John Taylor, written by Fife town planner Maurice Taylor, who drew on his memories of his own farming background to create the world of the Riggin.

Each story was illustrated by one of our most popular artists, Douglas Phillips. In his unique, lively and observant style, Doug captured the warm and homely feel of the stories perfectly, and thirty years later the series is still among the most popular features in the magazine.

This souvenir book is a chance for you to enjoy some more of our favourite stories and illustrations from "The Farmer And His Wife".

Contents

Pause For Thought

In Anne's Kitchen

Christmas On The Riggin

Dura Den.

John Taylor's Fife

Willie Shand explores the area of Fife immortalised in the "Farmer And His Wife" stories.

REGULAR readers of the "Friend" will know that it's a while now since John Taylor met his wife, Anne, and set up their farm on the Riggin.

You will no doubt be well acquainted with the farmer and his wife and with the places he often takes us to on his jaunts around Fife. His farm is set within that lovely part of the Kingdom known as the East Neuk – a neuk being a niche or a corner.

The hills here are quite tame in comparison with neighbouring Perthshire. Tame, but at the same time challenging, as you'll know if ever you've taken a walk from Dura Den and Kemback round by Blebo.

Largo Law doesn't even reach 1,000 feet high, yet is one of the East Neuk's most prominent landmarks. It's a bit of a scrauchle to attain its grassy summit, but on a clear day your efforts will be well rewarded. From the Law we indeed have "Prospect wide o'er field and fell" with the rich farmlands of the county spread out below.

Away to the south there's the Pentlands and the hills of Lothian, while westward your eye is drawn to the higher masses of Ben Lomond and round north to the Grampians.

Far out across the Firth of Forth we have grand uninterrupted views to the Bass Rock and away to the Isle of May – a prospect John frequently enjoys from his own fields.

Bounded on three sides by the waters of the Firth of Tay, the North Sea and the Firth of Forth, Fife has no shortage of coastal attractions, rugged cliffs giving way to wide sheltered bays and inviting sandy beaches, punctuated every now and then by charming old fishing ports like Crail, Pittenweem, Anstruther and St Monans.

Fife's climate and soils are well suited to arable farming with large acreages under wheat, barley, oats, turnips, potatoes and all sorts of other vegetables and fruits.

One could drive through Fife and almost never see a cow or a sheep – John's few cross-breeds excepted, of course.

Those who suffer from the effects of pollen might not be so thrilled to see the large fields of bright yellow flowering rape, but to the non-allergic photographer they offer endless opportunities.

I have my doubts if our John will ever have conquered the summit of the Law – it's just a wee bit steep for his buggy!

Living not far from the Law, though, he will, I'm sure, like most locals, find it an invaluable barometer – more reliable than any television forecast. As an old rhyme goes:

"When Largo Law puts on its cowl
Look out for wind and weather foul."

Up on the Riggin, they'll get a fair skelp of any wind that's going as it blows in from the North Sea. Straight from Siberia, as John often tells us!

Why is it the coldest blasts seem to come just as the newborn lambs arrive in the spring? Nature can be cruel sometimes.

For some 13 years I commuted back and forth from Kinross-shire to St Andrews and would often make wide detours through this more off-the-beaten-track countryside.

It's surprising how many different routes I could find to St Andrews. One favourite way would take me through Craigrothie, Ceres and Pitscottie.

If the old rhyme about the Law be true, it looks quite promising for today. Now and then, though, the east coast can be plagued with spells of haar.

Falls at Kemback.

St Monans.

One end of Cupar can be in beautiful sunshine under clear blue skies while the other end finds itself in pea-soup fog that only thickens the further east you go. There's every chance, though, that on days like that, the Law could still be poking its head above the murk.

Whichever road you choose to follow, you don't go far before reaching another wee town or village and most with enough interest to warrant stopping for a closer look.

Ceres is an old fermtoun steeped in stories from Fife's past. Archbishop Sharp went across its wee stone bridge in 1679, just before his ambush and murder on Magus Moor.

Not too unexpected a fate, I suppose, for possibly the most hated man in Scotland!

But Ceres's history stretches much further back than even this. Above the Green stands a granite memorial to the men of Ceres who marched off to join the Bruce at Bannockburn in 1314.

Their return is still celebrated each year in Ceres at Scotland's oldest Highland games.

Wherever I go, I love nosing through all the wee back streets and lanes. You just never know what you might stumble across.

Out this way even the milestones are unique – and accurate, too. The one in Kilconquhar is especially handy. It informs you that it's 0 miles to where you are!

In late summer, bright red poppies add splashes of vibrant colour to the verges, but there's one field in particular at a farm close to Kilconquhar where the poppies really must be seen to be believed.

One might imagine John struggling with the spelling of Kilconquhar – especially when it's pronounced nothing like it looks – "Kinneucher". As he admits, spelling was never his forte. You may recall him struggling with the word "fortnight" – he ended up just writing "two weeks"!

John's philosophy of early to bed, early to rise appears to have paid off. Besides, early morning is by far the best part of the day.

Long lies and days off are a bit of a luxury to any farmer with livestock to feed. Like shop-keepers, the farmer's day is never done – and it's seven days a week.

Few, though, would complain at that. It's just in the blood – or at least for the older generation.

Retirement? What's that? You just keep going as long as you're able.

St Andrews and Cupar are Fife's two principal towns and both have a long history. Cupar inherited the status of County Town away back in 1214.

In the centre of Cupar, where the Crossgate and Bonnygate meet, stands the mercat cross, and close by is the old Corn Exchange.

The Exchange was provided as a comfortable place for farmers to conduct the buying and selling of their agricultural products and implements.

The Exchange has passed its 150th anniversary, having been built in 1862.

It was on his way home from the Cupar Show that John apparently first met his wife-to-be, Anne.

Harvest can be a stressful time for those who rely on this as their main source of the year's income.

On any dry autumnal night, few farmers would not be out working the fields under tractor headlights.

With modern technology and machinery, you'd think life would become easier.

I doubt if many would welcome a return to the days of the Clydesdale horse, but as anyone visiting the Royal Highland Show will know, keeping abreast of modern technology certainly doesn't come cheap.

There are machines for everything. Gone are the days when kids could look forward to the tattie holidays to earn a bit extra pocket money.

Field entrances that would once have quite easily accommodated horse and cart are now widened to take larger modern machines, and fences provide a less costly alternative to the traditional dry stane dyke.

Tractors have grown into different beasts since the old grey Fergie. Changed days indeed since our John acquired his old Fordson with its cold and uncomfortable iron seat.

For all that, looking out from the summit of the Law, one might imagine the landscape of the East Neuk and that area we've come to know as the Riggin are pretty much timeless.

If you've never explored this part of Fife I'm sure it's an outing you really would enjoy. ■

On The Farm

Changed Days

On a cold day on the Riggin, I sit in Anne's kitchen and count my blessings!

AS I sit down to pen these notes to you – I say you, because you can be plural, but we like to think of you as just one person reading our life story – I'm very glad to be here in our warm kitchen.

It's the coldest day I've known for ages. It's dry, thank goodness, but the wind going past the Riggin, at what feels like 100 miles an hour, is what my granny would have called a lazy wind – it can't be bothered to go round, so it goes right through you!

I was well wrapped up, but it seemed to penetrate everything I had on.

Anne, bless her, knew what it was like to be out in that kind of a wind from a very early age. She would go out with her dad to round up sheep and bring them in to an inby field in case of a snow blizzard.

Because of the wind, Anne had decided we should have a hearty lunch. One to warm the cockles of your heart.

After I had thawed out, she placed a large bowl of oxtail soup on our large whitewood table. This was followed by a huge casserole of oxtail with mixed vegetables and mashed potatoes. It not only smelled good, but I can tell you it was fit for a king.

We didn't get up afterwards and rush to do the washing up. We sat for a while, Anne in her farmhouse chair, and me in my old, but very comfortable, winged chair.

And we thought how fortunate we were, when there are hundreds of people who never get a square meal. It's an unfair world, isn't it?

You have to be careful nowadays when you're entertaining. We both remember well the time Anne asked a local farmer and his wife for dinner.

She did them proud, making a steak and kidney hotpot with a delicious crust.

"Oh, Anne, I'm a vegetarian," the lady said, just as Anne was putting the food on the table.

Panic stations! All Anne could rustle up was baked beans on toast. It really put a damper on that evening's meal.

Coming back to the oxtail, I must tell you how Anne prepared it.

She always has cartons of stock in the deep freeze. Out came some beef stock.

When thawed, it went into the pressure cooker, with the oxtail, two large chopped onions, a bay leaf, a bouquet garni and a little garlic.

Anne has a tomato-shaped timer one of our grandsons gave her for Christmas. She set it to tell her when an hour had passed.

After cooling the pressure cooker under the tap, she added carrots, more onions, turnip and some grated cabbage.

The tomato timer was set for twenty minutes and in that short time all was ready for us to sit down and enjoy. And enjoy it I most certainly did!

I suppose, at my age, I should be thankful I have a memory at all. Well, I can't remember if I told you we are now in the jet age! I bought Anne a microwave oven.

Haven't we come a long way since everything was done on the open fire in the kitchen, with hot water boiler on one side and the oven on the other?

Happy days! ■

Feathering Our Nest

My Anne is no chicken when it comes to making business decisions!

WE hadn't been married long when Anne decreed that she was going to keep a dozen or so hens. My only condition was that the hen hut had to be far enough away from the farmhouse to ensure that the hens wouldn't stray up to the back door for scraps.

Hens strutting about a farmhouse back door may look idyllic on a birthday card, but you wouldn't believe the mess they make!

In our first year on the farm, Anne bought a dozen Rhode Island Reds at point of lay.

She made a good choice. Those hens were all good layers. But I pulled her leg and said she'd bought them because she liked their colour. They were a fine brownish shade, tinged with red.

She smiled. I knew I'd hit the nail on the head.

As well as the hens, she also bought a cock – a beautiful bird who strutted proudly round his harem.

"Why buy a cock," I asked, "if you only want the hens for their eggs?"

She looked at me and smiled.

"I'm going to breed and sell day-old chicks," she announced, and then went on, "and keep some for us."

I had visions of rows and rows of hen huts desecrating the landscape!

When I was a lad, there was a wee farm just below ours. The farmer and his wife had one son called Herbert. Poor lad, he was gawky and had a stutter.

Herbert and I started primary school on the same day. He sat on his gate waiting for me and we went to school together every day.

The other boys used to tease him because of his stutter, and once I remember he broke down in tears.

I tried to protect him.

Well, his mother and father took him to a doctor to see what they should do to help poor Herbert. The doctor's suggestion – "Get him something he can take a personal interest in." They decided on hens. Herbert, like Anne, started off with a dozen. He really made a study of hens. He wasn't the dumb character the boys at school made out.

By the time he was twenty-five, he was the largest egg producer in east Fife. A lorry came from Dundee every Thursday to take his eggs to the city.

When it became known that Anne and I were getting married and taking on our own farm, Herbert came to see me one evening. We went to inspect some young stock and were leaning over a gate when he said, "John, you'll be needing money to buy stock. Can I loan you some?"

The reason for this great gesture was, so I learned later, because I had fought for him at school, when other boys had tried to bully him.

I was really touched by his offer, but said we'd manage.

Anyway, to get back to Anne and her hens and cockerel. The following spring, she asked if I would knock her up some breeding pens. She was going into business.

Now, I've never been good at knocking up anything where it means putting a nail in straight. So I went to see a keeper who "knocked up" lots of pheasant pens every year. Oh yes, he would do the necessary.

Anne's first breeding season went very well and she sold lots of day-old chicks.

What I set off to tell you, but it's taken a long time, is that I bought Anne a new hen hut the other week – and not before time.

She smiled and thanked me. I saw a tear roll down her cheek. And I knew she was remembering her very first hen hut all those many moons ago. ■

A Good Old-fashioned Game!

Anne knocked spots off me when we dug out the dominoes!

I REMEMBER it well. It was a Tuesday and nothing had gone right. When I let the cows out to water, they didn't want to come in again, despite the rain. I wanted to be on my way to Cupar market with some fat lambs, and it was as if the cows knew that.

I was late for going through the ring and, therefore, late home.

I changed and was reluctant to leave Anne's warm kitchen to do the milking. But when I came back, I noticed the light was on in the stairs. In the kitchen, the table was laid, and something was simmering on the stove, but there was no sign of Anne.

I was surprised. You take your wife for granted, don't you?

I took my wellies off and hurried up the stairs, beginning to feel worried. Anne was on the floor in the spare room – playing dominoes!

She told me later that she had been looking for the silver gravy boat old George had given us for a wedding present.

"Do you need it for a dinner party?" I asked.

"No! It's just that I haven't seen it in years so I came upstairs to find it."

She hadn't – but she had found something else.

"Do you remember this tin, John?"

"Oh, yes," I said.

Really, I hadn't a clue, but I could tell by the way Anne spoke that I was supposed to.

The tin was about seven inches across and two inches deep. I suppose, in the early Forties, it held chocolates. There was a picture on the lid of men and women in Guards' uniforms.

And in the tin were the dominoes we used to play with when the kids were wee. Anne said it must have been thirty years since they'd seen the light of day. We were sorting out the dominoes when Anne remembered something.

"The stew will be burned!"

She fled downstairs, and I put the dominoes back in their tin and took it down with me to sample Anne's burnt offering. It wasn't really burned, by the way, just a bit stuck to the bottom of the pan.

After we washed up — and the pan took some doing — we had a game of dominoes at the kitchen table.

I lost hands down. Anne, in her young day, used to go to a lot of domino drives in the village hall, and she's a bit of an expert. There's more to playing dominoes than some people think.

We had played cribbage up until then, but now we are domino fans!

Oh, yes, and there's one more thing before I forget. We had a couple in for a meal last Saturday and Anne still couldn't find her silver gravy boat.

I know where it is, but I'm not going to tell her.

She felt sorry for Paul, shortly after his wedding, saying they hadn't much in the silver line, and she gave it to him!

It just goes to show that we all get older and a bit forgetful! ■

A Walk On The Wild Side

A stroll round the Riggin made me realise I'm not as young as I was!

I RECEIVED a telephone call the other day – which is very unusual, as all the calls are usually for Anne. It was one of nature's gentlemen – Willie, a retired gamekeeper, who now lives alone in a wee cottage in Crail. His wife, Jessie, died three years ago. She was a lovely lady. In fact, they were one of the nicest couples you could ever hope to meet.

They didn't have much money, but I bet they never owed a penny. They always set a good table, too, mainly off the land.

Thinking about that reminds me of the time, just after the war, when we were overrun by hares, not only on the Riggin, but over the whole East Neuk of Fife.

In the early spring, hare shoots were organised to reduce their numbers before the wheat and barley grew too high.

I will always remember one year – I think it was 1950 – when I was invited to join the shoot at David Simpson's farm, Wormiston.

On the morning of the shoot, Charlie McIntyre rang to say he might as well pick me up. Anne gave me the message when I came in from the yard.

I don't like being beholden to anyone, so I wasn't over the moon, but as Anne pointed out, I didn't want to get on the wrong side of Charlie as he worked for the Department of Agriculture. At the time, you wanted to stay on their good side as far as possible!

Charlie thought he was doing me a favour, but how I wished he hadn't bothered!

We had a really good shoot – over a hundred and thirty hares. That meant a lot more barley would reach the harvester.

David asked Charlie and myself in for a meal. I had never been to an after-shoot do before. There were drinks and more drinks, over which the shoot was discussed from start to finish.

Norah came to say supper was ready. Supper! It was a full-blown dinner taken at leisure! I was feeling a bit anxious that Anne would have to cope with the chores on her own.

I excused myself after the first course and rang her, suggesting she came to pick me up. She refused, saying Charlie would be offended.

So I stayed. We finally left at half-past eleven, but I took a hare home with me as a peace offering. We had it hot once, and there was so much meat left that Anne added onions, a few carrots, mixed herbs and gravy, and put it through a mincer.

I suppose nowadays it would be called hare pâté. It was just pressed hare, and with Anne's home-made chutney, it was a real treat.

Well, to get back to Willie's telephone call, which is what set me off reminiscing.

He asked if he could come up to the farm to see if there were any rabbits or hares about. It was one of those bright, clear, good-to-be-alive days when he arrived, so Anne suggested I walk round with him.

I don't often – well, all right, I never – walk round the farm all in one go.

Willie, I might add, is a good ten years older than I am, but he made me walk all that way – and carry the ferret!

When we got back, without any bag, he said, "Anne, John will sleep tonight. I bet he hasn't walked so far in the last twenty years!"

He was right on both counts – and Anne says I slept so soundly I didn't even snore! ■

This Little Piggy . . .

A piece in the paper made Anne and me look back to our early days on the Riggin.

ANNE'S the careful sort. As her mother used to say, "Don't spend a penny when half a penny will do!" Only she used to call it a bawbee, which is a Scots halfpenny.

Anne says we are extravagant, because we buy two local weekly papers.

Why? Well, where we live is called the Riggin of Fife – the saddleback of the East Neuk of Fife. If you look north you can see St Andrews and the Angus area; if you look south, you can see the Firth of Forth and East Lothian.

Anne plays bridge and does her shopping in St Andrews, so we get that local paper. The other one covers Crail, and the east coast parts. As Anne joins in the activities down there, too, we also buy it.

The St Andrews paper recently published a historical article, full of interesting agricultural facts and figures.

There was a piece about a farming family who kept four cows to supply the village with milk. They also had six pigs and two ponies which were used to take people into Cupar by trap. It cost tuppence for the ten-mile journey.

There was also a piece about piglet prices – two shillings for the runt of the litter to five shillings for a prime specimen.

I passed the article to Anne.

"What did I pay for that runt in 1934?" she asked.

I remembered it well . . . It was a Tuesday and I'd been going out with Anne for about a year. I met her in Crossgates, in Cupar, after the finish of the pig auction. Her face was all aglow. I could see she was bubbling over to tell me something.

"John, I've done as you said and bought a pig."

After church the previous Sunday, we'd discussed, as we pushed our bikes to Anne's farm, having to save money for a farm of our own. I'd suggested she should ask her dad to let her buy a pig and put it into their empty sty. He'd agreed.

"What are you paying?"

"Tom Summers said I could have the runt for eight shillings."

I suppose we all have to start at the bottom of the ladder – but to my mind this wasn't even *on* the ladder!

As I said, an economical sort, is my Anne. But I felt – although I didn't say it – that she would have done better to have paid a few shillings more for a better specimen.

"Will you come with me to collect it tonight, John?"

Dad let me take the farm buggy and off we went to Tom's for the runt. I told her on the way that she would have to buy another, as two do better than one on its own.

Tom's wife, Betty, said the same as we were leaning over the pig sty. Anne and Tom started a buying match for another piglet and Anne eventually paid twelve shillings.

Anne always had, and still has, a way with animals. Both those pigs thrived and did well. When they were ready for marketing, I asked when she would be taking them to Cupar Mart.

Anne had other ideas. Cupar Mart meant paying for transport – and then commission!

So Anne let it be known locally that she had two fat pigs for sale.

Uncle Jim and Aunt Mabel bought one, and paid her over the odds. Her dad bought the other.

Anne didn't bank all the money. She bought six more eight-week-old piglets! ■

Birds In Their Little Nests Agree . . .

. . . which is more than can be said for Anne and me sometimes!

ANNE and I had had one of those rows that shake the Riggin. But when you sit back and think, you wonder why two grown-up people should fall out over such a simple thing.

What were we fighting about? Well, you'll no doubt laugh when I tell you. Anne had tried to tell me I didn't know what I was talking about when I said a melon should be served in a bowl and not on a plate.

I knew what I meant, even if she didn't understand, and I was going to stick to my guns, regardless.

I could tell that Anne's pride wasn't going to let her back down, either, so after a while of getting nowhere I grabbed my old coat and stormed out.

Anne could get on with it on her own and put the darn thing on any plate she liked! All the same, it rankled, because I knew it should have been in a small pudding bowl.

It all started when Anne decided to ask two farming couples for a meal on a Saturday night. Anne enjoys company, and I don't mind helping out with preparing the grub.

As usual, we couldn't decide what to have for a starter. We never agree, and to be honest I don't know why Anne still bothers to ask me. I always suggest a good Scotch broth, which Anne ridicules, so my next choice is prawn cocktail.

On the night we fell out, Anne had decided on melon. Can you imagine anything more ridiculous?

We'd argued about the starter during Saturday night's dinner. If Anne and I are having melon on our own, which isn't often, we just cut it into slices.

However, if we're having company, Anne insists we present it in a very fancy way I think she must have read about in some of these glossy magazines.

Take it from me, it's a very fiddly business and I doubt if the guests ever appreciate what a long time it takes a poor soul to get just the right effect.

On this particular night, I cut the melon and was going to leave it to the guests to remove the skins.

"Oh, John, no!" Anne said in horror when she saw what I was doing. She wanted me to make it look posh.

I followed her instructions as best I could, then put the end result in bowls. That was when the fun began.

The Cambo Arms is about three miles away, or I would have been tempted to go and have a glass of the wine of Scotland, but instead – and probably more sensibly – I went into the byre and sat on a milking stool in the warmth.

I told the cows my story, but got no sympathy.

Instead, they gave me a look with their big eyes that said it all. We humans have a lot to learn from the beasts of the field and the birds of the air. ■

Watching The World Go By

Sometimes I like to stand and stare – but Anne says that makes me a nosy parker!

ANNE'S jealous. She can't get over the way I can lean over a gate and look at the view for ages. Or I can sit in a car and just watch the world go by. She's one of these people who always has to be up and doing – not wasting their time!

I agree with the poet who wrote:

"What is this life if, full of care,
We have no time to stand and stare?"

I enjoy watching nature. There's always something moving, if you keep still and watch.

One day, I was up in our top field leaning over a wall when I saw a curlew overhead. It dropped gently out of the sky and landed on a rough patch in the grass.

I noted where it landed. If it had a nest, it would be within ten yards or so. And I found it!

There were four beautifully marked eggs in it, pointed at one end so that they could not be blown out of the nest when the mother left it.

Well, I went back every day, hoping to see four fluffy curlew chicks. No luck. Then, one morning, when I arrived, there were broken eggshells, but no chicks. Ground-hatched birds can run shortly after birth.

Recently, we were out and about and Anne wanted to drop in on an old lady who lives in Kingsbarns. I said I'd wait in the square.

The square at Kingsbarns is well worth standing and admiring. There is a lovely church on one side, houses on another, and the east side is closed by a very nice house with a large garden. There's also a delightful old water-fountain to admire.

I was quite happy to wait there for as long as Anne wanted to take. I enjoy having time to myself.

As I turned into the square, I noticed there was a driving instructor in the process of giving a lesson. The pupil – a young girl – was trying to reverse the car and go around the fountain.

I sat and watched. I felt sorry for the lassie but I felt even more sorry for the fellow teaching her. I wouldn't be a driving instructor for all the tea in China.

Funnily enough, I'm actually the only member of our family who can't wave a piece of paper saying I'm fit to drive!

I learned to drive in our farmyard and across the fields in a succession of prehistoric tractors and cars – long before you had to sit a test, thank goodness!

I doubt if I could pass a test now – and I'm sure Anne would echo this view!

Well, Anne returned from her visit – and did I get it!

"How would you like to learn to drive with a nosy old fellow like you watching?" she asked. "It's hard enough trying to perform all those manoeuvres in a wee village square without having an audience into the bargain!"

I realised that – as usual – Anne was right. I shouldn't have sat in the square staring and embarrassing the lassie.

I just didn't think.

Anne says that's my trouble.

So, if the poor girl is reading this – I'm sorry! ■

Free-range feathered friends.

Domestic Bliss

The Come-In-Handy Box

It's amazing what you'll find a use for if you keep it long enough!

ANNE says I take after her father. He always maintained that, if you kept something for seven years, you would find a use for it. On their farm there was a wee calf hull. It was so wee and dark I don't think a calf had ever been brought up in it.

Into there, Anne's dad threw anything he thought might come in handy. It was so full of junk you could hardly get in . . .

I put things in wooden boxes under the stone benches in the dairy, instead!

Anne likes a wood fire in our sitting-room. The wood up beside the burn provides plenty of logs, but the timber has to be hauled home and cut up.

When I was a boy, two of us, with a cross cut and a saw stock, used to spend evenings cutting logs. Thank goodness someone invented the chain saw.

The other day I was busy cutting a fallen tree into logs. Even then I knew they would be too big for our fire.

I got the wedge to split them, but it had been hit so often by a sledge hammer that the edges were bent over and it got stuck in the log. I spent ages trying to get it out.

Then I remembered I'd once thrown the top of an axe whose shaft had split in one of the boxes in the dairy. It would do better than any wedge.

Talking of logs, years ago Anne and I had a day out to an auction in Leuchars.

Anne bought a large cauldron type of thing, made of beaten copper with a flute trim. I remember how badly it needed cleaning.

"What's it for?" I asked.

"Our Paul and Ruth's Christmas. It will look good full of logs by their lounge fire."

When the sale was over we took it home. Anne cleaned it and filled it with logs – just to see how it would look.

I can't remember how long ago it was that we bought that wee cauldron, but that copper log holder is still sitting beside our fireplace. Sorry, Paul. Sorry, Ruth.

As I sat on the old milking stool in our dairy, rummaging in that box for the axe-head, I came across something else. It must be an antique; we've had it so long.

It was a very light, aluminium jelly mould. In the shape of a rabbit. I could just imagine Anne looking at it and not having the heart to throw it in the dustbin.

She used to make a bunny jelly for every bairn's birthday party, and another at Christmas. There was always an argument about who got the head and who got the tail.

Anyway, while I was searching for the axe-head Anne came into the dairy and I showed her the bunny mould. She laughed.

"Do you remember? At one party a wee lassie – about four – kicked up such a fuss that her mum had to take her home. She wanted the tail."

I smiled, too.

Next teatime Anne made an orange jelly. And she opened a tin of mandarin oranges and mixed them into the jelly.

"Just for old times' sake," she said. ■

Labour Of Love

When Anne decides something needs done, she doesn't hang about!

IF Anne gets a bee in her bonnet about doing something, she does it right away. In our hall stand the first pieces of furniture we ever bought – an old oak settle and a chair. Anne bought the chair at a sale years and years ago – and for a song compared with present-day prices.

Anne and I still enjoy going to a sale, although we don't get to as many these days.

It's always interesting to see what's going under the hammer, and you can more often than not pick up a real bargain, if you know what you're looking for.

I was sitting by the kitchen stove the other evening when she came in, carrying the chair.

"It needs a new seat, John. This looks faded."

I admitted that it did look a bit tatty.

"Where did we put that left-over piece of Blue Boy?"

There was a period in time, more than thirty years ago, when Blue Boy tapestry was all the rage, and Anne went daft for it. We had so much there was bound to be some left over.

I was left in peace for about half an hour until she came back into the kitchen, all smiles.

Annie had found the piece of Blue Boy in the odds-and-ends drawer, but she'd found something else there as well.

She unwrapped the faded tissue paper and held up a coloured pompom made of wool.

It was as good as new, despite being over seventy years old – and what memories it brought back!

I must have been about ten when I made the thing, and I remember how proud I was of my achievement.

It went into the next church sale. The price asked for this work of art was one shilling and sixpence.

It was bought by Miss McAndrew, who came and congratulated me on my contribution to church funds.

When our son, Paul, was born, Miss McAndrew came to visit Anne and brought the same ball in the same tissue paper as a gift. I don't know why we didn't pass it on to Mary when she presented us with our first grandchild.

We have decided to give it to the first of our grandchildren who makes us great-grandparents. That makes us sound like two Methuselahs, doesn't it?

Do bairns nowadays make such things for church sales? Anne says that, for the next one, I should make another pompom for old times' sake.

I think I'll just send the usual bag of tatties!

But I've digressed from the repair of the actual seat.

Although she has done it now, Anne actually never did get round to it at the time as, two days later, a letter arrived from Mary asking for Anne's help.

She'd enclosed a knitting pattern entitled "Teddies For Tragedies". Mary's church Guild had been asked to knit teddies to send to children in need. Would Mum like to knit one?

You can guess the answer.

It took her three nights and I was proud of the finished article. I hope it brings happiness to some little girl or boy. ■

Proving A Point

I'm the worst husband for miles around, or so Anne tells me!

THERE are times when I wonder why Anne married me. I bet she wonders the same. She didn't know me as well then as she does after living over 40 years with me!

Looking back, things were totally different in the late Thirties, when we got married, from nowadays.

We were never allowed to go to dances and, therefore, I cannot dance. Oh, I can go round a dance floor with Anne, but no thank you, no-one else. I've just about got the hang of one dance – the Gay Gordons. It's the one where you take so many steps forward then back and the lady twirls round.

I do that dance if the floor is covered and only the couple behind can see that John Taylor still hasn't quite grasped even the Gay Gordons.

Both Anne and I regret that we didn't learn to dance. Not that we would have been going to the jigging every Saturday night, but perhaps once or twice in the year at Farmers' Dances.

Still, according to Anne, I am the only farmer in the East Neuk of Fife who cannot dance.

We were sitting round the stove one Saturday night. Anne had finished her knitting – a big, thick brown pullover for one of the boys – and hadn't anything on the needles.

There was nothing worth watching on television – there never seems to be on a Saturday night.

I said as much to Anne.

"Well, what's the point in putting good programmes out on a Saturday when everyone is out somewhere? I bet we're the only two in tonight," she retorted.

I know we're odd, but I don't believe all the other farmers in East Neuk were at a dance, the theatre, a pub or just out for dinner.

Without saying a word to Anne, I went across to the phone and dialled a number I knew by heart.

"Who are you ringing?" Anne demanded, but I didn't answer.

"Hello, is that you, Norah? Is Jimmy about?"

"Yes, he's about, John. Is it urgent? I can't bring him to the phone as he's making marmalade and daren't leave it. I'll get him to give you a ring later."

"Don't bother, Norah, but hold on, Anne wants a word with you."

Anne gave me a filthy look but, give her her due, came to the phone.

"Hello, Norah," she began, and the pair of them managed to find something to talk about for the next 20 minutes. So much for the bill!

When she came off the phone, Anne let me have it, but it was like water off a duck's back as I had made my point – Norah and Jim were in and Jim was even making the year's marmalade on a Saturday night.

Apparently, every farmer in East Neuk also plays bridge, with the exception of yours truly.

"If you wouldn't be so stubborn and just learn, we could have other couples in to play. And we would be asked out," Anne complained one day.

Would we? I've no proof we would. Now, how could I carry out a poll, or whatever you call it, to find out how many farmers in this area do not play bridge?

If 10 per cent of them do, I'd be surprised. I bet they've been goaded into playing by their wives.

You see how I wonder why Anne married me?

I daren't even try to learn to play bridge, because I'd make such a mess of it that Anne would be madder than ever.

To hear Anne talk, I'm the worst husband around – but I think she would miss me . . . ■

Picture This

My new painting brightened up our home in more ways than one!

IN the old days, we just used to walk into the doctor's surgery. We always knew the times as Anne had them pinned up in the kitchen. Now, however, you have to ring them up and ask for an appointment. So, the other week when I wasn't feeling quite up to scratch, I did just that.

After a little bit of friendly persuasion, the receptionist said she could fit me in that afternoon at the end of the queue.

I duly presented myself at the busy surgery, already feeling better, as usually happens, nodded to one or two people I knew, and looked around for something to read.

There is usually a wide selection of magazines, but I rarely see one that I like. However, that day someone had left quite an interesting catalogue of antiques.

I thumbed through its pages. Not that I'm an expert on antiques, but Anne knows her furniture and has had some good bargains over the years.

I came across a page with illustrations of various pictures for sale. I was really taken by one in particular. It was a farmyard scene and I liked it so much I decided I must order it.

A couple of weeks later, the farm study I'd so admired duly arrived and when it did, Anne and I had to laugh. It was beautifully drawn and coloured, but very small.

How could I make it into a real picture? That evening, I tried all sorts and sizes of mounts, but eventually I had to concede defeat.

Anne and I later took it to a picture-framer in St Andrews that we have used in the past. We trust his judgement. He recommended a simple oak frame.

We also had a brass plate inscribed with the artist's name and the date.

In case you're wondering what the point of the story is, let me shed some light on it, so to speak.

Anne hung the picture on the upstairs landing, above a half round table, which has a few bits and pieces on it.

There's also an electric light switch under the picture. A daft place to put the switch, I've always said, as you have to grope your way along the landing to turn it on.

Well, a few nights later, Anne dug me in the ribs as we lay in bed. I woke up at once.

"John, there's someone on the landing!"

Anne had been awake and had noticed that the landing light had come on. Well, she was right.

I switched on our bedside light, picked up a brass candlestick from the dressing-table and opened the bedroom door.

Yes, the landing light was on, but there was no sign of any intruder. I went all over the house, but all the doors were locked.

It wasn't until the next day that we found out who had put on the light . . .

My new picture was the culprit. The string had snapped and, as the picture fell to the floor, it had flicked on the light switch.

I suppose if the picture had been as big as I'd first thought, the noise of it falling would have alerted us.

As it was, the little picture just dropped off the wall with no noise to speak of!

Anne, of course, maintained it was my fault. I thought she meant for buying the picture in the first place, but it seems I should have gone round all the pictures checking their strings.

You can't win, can you? ■

Take Your Medicine

If only there was a pill to stop me putting my foot in it!

LIKE many other people, we keep our medicine chest in the bathroom. I cut my finger quite badly one day and, as I didn't want to alarm Anne, I sneaked up the stairs to the bathroom. But when I opened the door of the cabinet to look for some plasters or a bandage, a bottle fell out.

Luckily for me, it didn't break.

When I finished attending to my finger – which wasn't as bad as I had thought – I tried to put the bottle back, but couldn't find space for it.

Promising myself I'd come back and spring-clean, I went downstairs carrying an empty bottle labelled *4711*.

"What's the point in keeping empty bottles cluttering up the shelves?" I demanded of Anne.

You'd think I'd have learned to keep my big mouth shut by now, wouldn't you?

"John Taylor! You mean you don't remember buying it?"

It had been a long time ago. Anne and I weren't yet married. What should I give her for her birthday?

After a cattle auction in Cupar, I visited a chemist and the lassie there was very helpful. I came out of that shop with a spring in my step and a bottle of perfume wrapped in pretty gift paper tucked into my jacket pocket.

"That was the first personal present you ever gave me," Anne told me.

Even after all that time, I felt quite chuffed to have got it right. She must have liked the gift, or she wouldn't have kept the bottle for all those years, would she?

Up till then, I suppose our presents had been what you might call practical. Anne had given me two good sheep, and I had given her a table and a stool.

The stuff in our medicine cabinet is practical, too.

Anne's not one for spending money on stuff to put on her face. She's a careful sort. She has a wee box of powder with a puff and a lipstick and that's all.

She doesn't even use these very much. The last time I saw her try to make up her face was when we were going to the Farmers' Ball in Cupar.

Anne had put her gladrags on, and then did her face.

"How's that, John?"

I looked at her. Should I be truthful, or just tell her she looked fine, for the sake of a quiet life?

I was truthful. Anne disappeared in a huff.

I still think I did the right thing. She has one of those rugged country complexions that many pale-skinned town ladies would pay dearly for. A lot of make-up looks all wrong, and she doesn't need it anyway – or I don't think she does.

But maybe I could have been a bit more tactful . . .

Ah, well, back to the bathroom. I'm going to give the chest a good clear-out.

How's your medicine cabinet? Does it need spring-cleaning, too? ■

There's Many A Slip . . .

It's never too late to learn a new skill, as I discovered to my cost.

ANNE had agreed to meet me at the car in Cupar at 12.30 p.m. Already it was twenty to one and there was no sign of her. At 12.50 she came rushing round the corner with her shopping.

"Sorry I'm late, my watch had stopped."

A pretty poor excuse, as anyone who knows Cupar in Fife will tell you that from nearly every point in the main street you can see the clock on the old town hall.

She piled her parcels on to the back seat and I started the engine.

"Oh, John, before we go, please look at this," she said. It was one of those packets with a paper cut-out pattern. "How do you like it?" she asked eagerly.

On the front was a drawing of a young thing who looked as though she needed a good meal and was about 20 years younger than Anne.

To me it was merely a dress, so I said yes, I liked it.

She hadn't wanted to buy any material until I'd seen the pattern – so would I wait two minutes whilst she nipped up the street?

Half an hour later, she finally reappeared clutching a parcel.

On the way home, she couldn't resist showing me her bargain.

Well, it proved to be far from a bargain – not in money terms, but in tears, sweat, temper, late meals and late nights.

There's no time like the present with my Anne. I opened the sitting-room door to find a blazing fire and the chairs all pushed back. The dress material was spread out on the floor and the paper pattern spread over it.

After having a wash, I sat in an armchair and just watched. From my elevated position, I could see trouble. I passed comment on the position of the two halves of the back.

My comments were ignored. I kept quiet thereafter.

One does not, if one values matrimonial bliss, say "I told you so." It's better just to think it and keep quiet.

"John, what can I do?" she wailed. "The back doesn't match."

That's what I'd been trying to point out earlier.

Then came the tears. So I had to get out of my armchair, get down on my hands and knees and help.

By the end of the evening, the top half had been tacked together, minus sleeves. How did I like it, Anne wanted to know.

"Dear, isn't it a bit tight?" I suggested tactfully.

It gave Anne one of those uplifts you don't mind seeing on other fellows' wives, but not on your own. I was informed that when the skirt part was added it would come all right.

The next night she tacked the sleeves. One was taken out and adjusted. When it was tacked in again it was too tight.

It took two late nights to get those sleeves almost right. The skirt half was soon cut out and run up, but it was too tight and had to be taken to bits.

To cut a long story short, the dress was completed after four late nights. It had its first outing at a sale of work on behalf of our local church.

The minister's wife asked where Anne had bought her dress. I think that was the most tactful remark I've ever heard her make. What Anne would have said if she'd been asked if she had run it up herself, I shudder to think.

One last word of advice – if you aren't an expert at this running-up-a-dress lark, please, for your husband's sake, buy a simple pattern! ■

Lest We Forget

You know you're getting old when your memory starts playing tricks on you!

Do you find that, as you get older, your memory isn't quite what it was? I certainly do, and Anne's just as bad – but she won't admit it! Recently, she said she wanted the guest bedroom decorated. It was needing a wee freshen up, she told me. That's a joke. It's thirty years since that room was papered!

Anne spent two hours going through books of paper. Why can't women just look and say, "I like that"?

Instead it's always, "How do you like that?"

To be honest, I didn't mind which paper was chosen, but by the time I went to bed, Anne had five bits of paper jutting out of the book for me to choose from in the morning!

However, I've lived with Anne long enough to know how to go about the business of choosing.

"Which would you like, dear?"

Anne flicked through the book and stopped at a page.

"How do you like this?"

"Just right for that room, dear." I couldn't have cared less, but it's as well to show an interest.

I couldn't have said it convincingly enough.

"Do you think I get should some more books, dear?" Anne asked me brightly.

I declined in no uncertain terms.

Eventually, we decided on that first paper. Which is exactly what I knew would happen all along!

Well, paper chosen, D-Day arrived. The decorator was coming in the morning.

The young man duly arrived. To give him his due, he set straight to work, and with only a short break for lunch, put all the paper on in one day.

Anne, who is of course an expert, said he used too much paste.

He left on the Friday night, and by Saturday morning, the paper still wasn't dry. Perhaps Anne was right about the paste.

She instructed me to carry a heater into the room to dry it out. To my simple mind, it would have dried out eventually by itself, but who am I to express an opinion? I have long since learned that it's quicker to do what Anne asks!

After lunch on Saturday, we were going to Berwick-upon-Tweed to stay with a farmer friend. We were just driving across the Forth Road Bridge when Anne said suddenly, "John, did you remember to turn off the heater?"

"Yes, dear."

Then came the doubt. Had I? I couldn't remember doing it. Hadn't I? Would it go on fire before Sunday night?

After tea, I went out with Calum, our host, to inspect his sheep. I told him I was worrying, and why.

He laughed and said he was glad he wasn't the only one with a bad memory.

To cut a long story short, we went back to his office, and, without a word to the women, I phoned our neighbour.

He very kindly agreed to take our spare key and nip next door to check that the house hadn't burned down. Within half an hour he had called back.

"John, that paper will be dry. What a heat in that room!"

I never told Anne I hadn't remembered to turn off the heater. It would never have been an issue if we'd just left the paper to dry in its own time.

And after all, I'd said, "Yes, dear," in good faith – it's just that my memory isn't what it was thirty years ago. ■

As Fresh As Paint!

I had to dive for cover when Anne had the decorators in!

I MUST be getting weak in my old age. Anne had been going on for a while about the inside window-sill needing a touch-up — could she get a painter in?

For the sake of peace I just grunted my agreement. I must be a complete nincompoop, because the windows were just Anne's excuse to get a painter on the premises! Every room was gone through.

"Can you cover that crack in the ceiling?"

"Yes, but a bathroom really needs two or three coats."

The lounge, dining-room, bedrooms and kitchen were all included.

The poor painter, pencil and pad in hand, stood waiting for Her Ladyship's instructions. At last she was done, and he asked if he should give us an estimate.

"Yes, please."

It's not often I go against Anne, but I chipped in.

"Don't bother, just come and do it. And if your man tells me what I owe as he walks out the door, I'll pay him cash."

Anne and I pay as soon as a job is done. We owe no-one and we often get a discount for cash.

But, on this occasion, Anne branded me hopeless.

"Have you got money to burn? Why didn't you get an estimate?"

I'm not as green as I'm cabbage-looking. I knew the painter would hardly be through the door before Anne would be asking, "Will you just freshen up that wall there while you're at it?"

If he had given an estimate, he would have doubled it to cover himself. He knew that and so did I.

A young lad duly arrived and began on Anne's list of jobs. He insisted that everything should be moved out of each room he was painting — in fact, he only let us in with a brolly for protection!

As the only two places not being done were the hallway and my wee office, you can guess we were in a terrible muddle.

The kitchen was full of items from other rooms so we went into

St Andrews for our meal.

When we got back to the Riggin, Anne suddenly remembered.

"Oh, John, I've asked the painter if he'll do the larder."

"It will take two hours for him to empty the larder – all that money for no decorating at all!"

So I spent two hours putting everything into boxes and taking them across to the dairy. Lots of tasty things. Some of them would surely disappear before they saw the larder again.

I lifted the larder shelves off so that the painter could get right in to the walls. I would be out working next day, so it was up to Anne to deal with him. I told Anne he had to be finished by five p.m. or she would be paying the bill.

He'd have to be out by then or I couldn't put the larder back in order. That, to me, is the most important room in the house – or so my tummy always tells me! ■

Floored Again!

When Anne decided she wanted new kitchen flooring, I knew better than to argue . . .

I'VE little doubt that our kitchen floor was originally stone flags. When we took over at the Riggin, the floor was covered with black and white lino squares. It looked really modern, but Anne couldn't keep them clean.

Then she saw an advertisement for an auction of second-hand carpets in St Andrews. There was a large Axminster for sale, measuring fifteen feet by eighteen feet.

Not many homes could accommodate a carpet of that size, Anne said. She got me to measure the kitchen floor. It was just right for us.

At the sale, the auctioneer couldn't get a bid. He was just about to pass on it when Anne put up her hand and offered three pounds. To her delight, the carpet was knocked down to her.

It was definitely worth it. The carpet has only recently begun to show its age – and the pounding it's had from my eighteen stones!

Anne has hinted on a number of occasions that we should do something about it. To keep the peace, I always agree with her, but I haven't got round to doing anything about it yet.

Then she went out to tea with a friend who lives in St Andrews.

"John, you should see her new kitchen floor!"

On and on she went.

I broke in and asked the size of that kitchen – I've seen some that are overcrowded with two people.

The subject was dropped – but not for long.

The following week, Anne came home and handed me something she called a carpet tile. I examined it. It seemed tough and hard-wearing – just right for the kitchen.

I also saw another advantage to it. If I spilled something like pickled beetroot on it, I could just replace one or two tiles.

So a man came to measure the floor.

"I want the tiles to go under there," Anne said, pointing to the fridge and washing-machine and the cupboard under the worktop.

The man looked doubtful.

"I don't think it'll go under the cupboard. It's too tight." Then he got out of the problem by adding, "Discuss it with the men when they come to lay the tiles."

When the men came, their first task was to take up our old carpet.

"Should I send it to the saleroom?" Anne asked.

"No," I said. "I've asked the men to put it on the tip."

I must admit, I felt a pang of regret, but our old carpet really was finished.

"I'm sorry, but we can't put tiles under that cupboard. There isn't enough room," the chief carpet-layer said.

The offending cupboard was in the centre of the room. Anne and I looked at each other. It was obvious that the kitchen would be tidier without it. But what would we do with the contents?

The drawers at the top held tea towels, dusters and odds and ends galore. Below, on two shelves, were pans, cooling trays, cake tins of all sizes, four sieves, two mincers and lots more stuff we've collected over the years.

We had a grand clear-out. Some things went into the dustbin, others into the church sale. We got the rest into other cupboards, except for the big jam pan, which went into the dairy. By the way, the kitchen looks a lot better. ■

Count Your Blessings

As I watched Anne hang out the washing, I realised how lucky we are . . .

"JOHN, did you listen to the weather forecast?"

Are you like me? I listen, and then wonder what was said for our area. I always manage to lose the thread.

Anne was already stripping the bed. I could only presume that, whatever the forecast, she was going to wash.

In the old days, Monday was always washing day, regardless of the weather. Now – well, it doesn't matter, does it?

Electricity made all the difference to washing day. Can you remember the boiler in the washhouse, with the wee fire underneath which had to be kept stoked?

Anne says nowadays housewives don't know how lucky they are. Put the clothes in the machine, add the detergent and press the switch. Child's play!

It comes out spun-dry – or even completely dry, if you have a tumble dryer. Great if it's wet outside!

Before the press of a switch, Anne and I had "the perfect answer."

Our Valor Perfection stove had two long blue funnels and, if you were posh, you had an oven which sat, when required, on top. I wonder what today's housewives would think of the paraffin smell?

And would they take the paraffin tin to the local shop for a gallon and then, with a funnel, fill the tank?

We also had an Aladdin's lamp; then we got one with a small mantel which you blew up with a pump.

It had a wee hole between light and tank and you had to prick this hole with a very thin wire.

Dad always did the lamps on a Sunday afternoon in the kitchen. One day he lit one and there was a mighty bang. The hole must have been blocked. The lamp blew up and went on fire.

There were clothes on a pulley hung from the ceiling. They caught fire and fell on Dad. He hadn't much hair at the best of times, but he had less that Sunday night.

But it was his hands that were worst. They had really caught the blast.

We had no phone, of course, so we couldn't get the doctor. Instead, I was sent to the next farm to get a thick, yellowy ointment. Mother dotted Dad's hands with it and bandaged them up.

I can't think who did the milking that night. Or, for that matter, for a good few nights.

Anne says I'm really annoying in my old age. Well, perhaps I am, but recently I had reason. I came in for my morning drink to find Anne using a fork to whisk the eggs for a custard.

"Where's your whisk?" I asked. Anne's mother had given it to us years ago.

"It's broken."

I got it out. Anne was right. It was broken. The gears didn't catch and it either jumped or came to a full stop.

I was so annoyed that Anne, at her age, should have to whisk an egg with a fork that I went straight to an electrical shop in St Andrews.

They were most helpful. I came away with a gadget with two whisks which fly round on three speeds. And I was surprised how cheap it was!

Anne was delighted.

P.S. I've just read this story to Anne. She says not to put the egg custard in too hot an oven; rather when it's cooling off. And don't forget to sprinkle a little nutmeg on top! ■

Anne keeps a meadow to attract the bees.

Weighty Matters

Brace Yourself!

Sometimes a man feels the need for a bit of support . . .

JOHN, you'll really have to get a new suit."

When Anne made that statement, something told me she didn't know the price of suits these days. And she confirmed my suspicions by following it up with: "And you'll have to have it made. Nobody does your size off the peg."

I was immediately on the defensive.

"I've only had this suit for a couple of years – and I'm not Andrew Carnegie!"

"Two years, my foot!"

Well, whether it had been two or ten years, there's no doubt that I made a big mistake when I bought that suit. And it was all my own fault.

I remember trying it on and noticing there were no buttons for braces. I said as much to the skinny salesman.

"Oh, you don't need buttons in this day and age, sir. You have clip-on braces."

I should have put my foot down, but I gave way. That was quite unusual for me. In fact, my daughter refuses to go into a shop with me because she never knows what I'll do or say.

I was brought up to ask for a luck penny for cash – in other words, a discount. I still get it sometimes.

But to get back to my suit . . .

Those clip-on braces seemed to get weaker and weaker. They would have been fine on my working trousers, which had plenty of give around the tummy, but my new suit just seemed to get tighter and tighter!

Finally, one day when I was getting ready to go to a funeral in Arncroach, the braces "went" altogether – ping! And there was nothing I could do!

Anne and I did manage to solve the problem in a none-too-dignified way, and off I went to the funeral. And it was when I came back that Anne made the announcement that I was going to have to buy a new suit.

Now I wasn't convinced that there was anything wrong with the suit – although I admit it was tight.

I didn't say anything to Anne, but I quietly decided it wasn't a new suit but good, old-fashioned buttons and real braces that I needed.

If they didn't solve my problem I would have no option but to go on a crash diet. No way was I buying a new suit.

I went to a men's outfitters which deals with large-sized farmers. There were no skinny young modern chaps in there waving away my request and trying to fob me off with unsuitable merchandise! They are used to dealing with old-fashioned chaps like me who are a bit too fond of their grub.

I asked for long braces with leather bits for buttons.

To my joy and amazement, the sales assistant didn't look at me in a pitying manner. He brought out the proper braces that I wanted, and now I can go anywhere without worrying about gravity, or how much cheese I had for supper.

When I took them home and showed them to Anne, she just shook her head and laughed.

At my age, what do I need a new suit for, anyway?

By buying those new braces, I saved myself a few hundred pounds on a new suit. And that amount of money doesn't grow very fast in our Riggin fields nowadays! ■

Say Cheese!

Yes, please, that's what I say – but only if Anne doesn't find out!

ANNE tries every dodge she can think of to get my weight down. I know she's only doing it for my own good, but it goes against the grain. I'm a grown man, after all. I like to think I can manage my own eating habits, but I daren't say that in front of Anne!

"If you could manage your own diet you wouldn't be eighteen stone, John Taylor!"

Anne had recently been visiting a friend who had suffered a heart attack. She, like me, loved to eat.

Anne said the doctors had told Alice to lose weight and that the best way to do it was to eat little and often. I agreed with the "often" part, but was more doubtful about "little".

One of my biggest downfalls is cheese. I love it. Often, as I pass the fridge, I will open the door and break a goodly lump off the piece of cheese in there just to munch on as I go about the yard.

Once, when Anne and I were visiting relations in Kirkby Lonsdale, I bought a whole Stilton from a wonderful little delicatessen we found there.

Anne almost hit the roof, but I was delighted with my purchase. We ate every scrap and I was sorry when it was finished.

I don't think there is any type of cheese I don't like. Anne says it's not good for my weight, and she tries to make sure I don't eat too much of it.

Mind you, she also complains that I snore when I have been eating it, so perhaps there is more than concern for my health behind her plan to make me cut down!

I particularly like the crumbliness of Lancashire cheese. It also has a tang I love, but I can't buy it any more. If I break a bit off, it leaves tell-tale crumbs on the floor!

Ladies, may I give you a bit of advice? Six-thirty in the morning is not the best time to find fault with your loved one. He's not in the best of tempers at that time of day.

"Did you enjoy the cheese last night?"

Before I had gone up to bed the night before I had decided a little snack would help me to sleep better.

I made a quick sandwich of the tasty Lancashire cheese on fresh bread with plenty of butter. And I really enjoyed it.

I had been in such a hurry to get upstairs and not rouse Anne's suspicions that I had missed some of the crumbs on the floor.

As always, Anne's eagle eye had spotted the evidence. My solution? Buy a hard cheese if you don't want to be caught out!

Recently, one of our grandsons was invited to a works party and the burning question was, what should he take?

I suggested an Orkney cheese and Anne suggested a plant.

My suggestion was dismissed out of hand.

"Box of chocolates, then?"

"A thing of the past," I was told.

We spent the evening, or at least, Anne did, trying to work out what he should take to the party.

In the end, he pushed the boat out and did his boss proud. He went for the Scottish option and took a rich fruitcake and a bottle of twelve-year-old malt.

Anne and I have decided that we are really back numbers when it comes to young people's idea of a perfect present.

We would have taken one or the other – to us, taking both was simply an extravagance.

As we lay in bed that night, Anne asked, "John, are we mean?"

"No, dear," I told her. "It's just we're living now in an age where money is to be spent, not saved." ■

Food For Thought

A trip to the supermarket shows me fruits I've never even heard of!

ARE you going into Kingsbarns this morning, John?"

To be honest, it hadn't been my intention, but by the tone of Anne's voice, it looked like I would be going now.

"I want Dorothy to get this tomorrow," she explained.

On the previous Sunday, we had been invited to Tony and Dorothy's for lunch – and very enjoyable it was, too, despite Anne reminding the hostess that I was on a strict diet!

We started with soup, followed by a casserole of pork and potatoes, followed by biscuits and cheese.

Anne saw to it that Tony and I didn't discuss farming – well, not for too long, anyway!

We left at about half-past three, and we both agreed it had been a very enjoyable lunch. Hence the thank-you note that Anne was anxious to get to Dorothy.

If Anne is giving a lunch or dinner, she makes sure that she plans everything well in advance.

She says if you choose your menu sensibly and do all your preparation beforehand, you can bring it to the table as if it's been no effort at all.

One day I was in Perth at the auction mart and noticed a supermarket nearby, so after the auction I went in. I enjoy a bit of shopping on my own, although Anne and I have fallen out over what I bring home!

I collected a trolley and ambled round. There were out-of-season strawberries from America and lots of exotic fruits that I don't think even Anne would know what to do with.

As I wandered round, I couldn't help noticing what some young mothers were filling their trolleys with – ready-made microwave meals and lots of tins – nothing that called for much cooking.

I couldn't help wondering what my old granny would have made of it. And are we any better for the change in eating habits? I doubt it.

A good, plain diet, such as Anne dishes up, has brought us both to over eighty, so it must have done some good.

I enjoy my grub, and a hard day's work on the farm certainly works up an appetite. I look forward to coming home at night to see what Anne is going to serve up.

Whether it's a nice mixed grill or tripe and onions, I know it's going to be out of this world.

I certainly wouldn't be happy if I came in from a day at the lambing to be confronted by one of these measly little microwave meals in a plastic tray!

Mind you, I'm still overweight. The doctor keeps telling me to lose two stones but, as any of you who are in the same boat will know, it's easier to put it on than to lose it!

I didn't come out of the supermarket that day with an empty trolley. No, my purchases amounted to a large packet of washing powder, pads for scrubbing pans – my job – a chicken and lots of fruit.

I've been given a diet sheet – chicken, fish, fruit, beans, potatoes (thank goodness), but no cakes or anything with sugar.

I can still have porridge for breakfast and toast with sugar-free marmalade. I have lost some weight and, I must admit, I do feel the better for it. ■

The Battle Of The Bulge

I've been playing the weighting game most of my life!

ABOUT three years after we were married, Anne and I were invited to a dinner and dance.

Anne wanted to go. I'm not a dancer, so I wasn't keen. But, needless to say, we went!

I wore my best – and only – suit, and Anne made herself a long dress. After a very enjoyable evening, Anne remarked that there had only been three men in lounge suits.

"We must get you an evening suit before next year," she decided.

We were just starting out on the Riggin, struggling to keep above the red line at the bank, and here was Anne talking about buying a penguin suit!

Well, I got one eventually, and it lasted about twenty years. Then, because of Anne's good cooking, I just couldn't get the trousers to meet!

By then we were going to three dinner-dances a year, so I was instructed to go to be measured for a new penguin suit.

Last year, Anne was invited to go, with a friend and her husband, to some do in St Andrews. She didn't commit herself, bless her.

She said she would ask me first, though I knew she was keen. She dug out a long frock for me to pass opinion on!

About two o'clock next morning, when I was lying awake, I suddenly wondered if I could still get into the trousers of my penguin suit.

I knew I'd never get to sleep if I didn't set my mind at rest. So I got up in the dark, and it was just as I'd feared – they wouldn't go near me!

Next morning, Anne phoned our friends to say how sorry we were.

I didn't say anything to Anne, but when I weighed myself, I was concerned at how heavy I'd become.

A friend of mine had told me how he regained his sylph-like figure by going on a grapefruit diet.

He had bought crates of the stuff at a fruit market in Edinburgh and had one before every meal.

I decided to follow his example, but I wasn't quite so drastic. I started having a grapefruit for my breakfast and a glass of juice before every meal.

Then, about six one morning, I began to get pains in my chest.

I didn't say anything to Anne, but I went into the kitchen for a glass of juice to see if it would make the pain disappear. It didn't.

In the end, it got so bad I had to tell Anne.

"All you've got, John, is acidity."

But to make quite sure, she told me to go to the doctor. I was so worried, I agreed.

Once in the surgery, the doctor checked me over and made me get on the scales.

"Don't worry about the pain in your chest, Mr Taylor," he said finally. "It's only acidity. But you know you're too heavy, don't you? Here's a diet sheet. I want you to stick to it."

I did, too, and now I can get my penguin trousers on! What a pity we haven't anywhere to go that I can wear them. Perhaps at Christmas . . . ■

John likes his greens!

Family & Friends

Guess Who's Coming To Tea?

Nothing was too much trouble when our son brought his girlfriend home!

JOHN TAYLOR, you were dragged up!"

Having seen it in print, I realise that it looks worse than it sounded at twelve o'clock on a Saturday night!

We had been over to Bill and Marion's for dinner – and a very nice dinner it was, too. Marion had been to a lot of trouble, but the evening went so smoothly it seemed as if everything just appeared out of thin air.

We drove out of the yard and Anne said, "I must give Marion a ring to say thank you. No – I'll drop her a note."

"Darling, I thanked them for a very enjoyable evening. Is there any need to write?"

That was when the infamous statement was uttered. I was told, in no uncertain terms, that that wasn't enough. Writing a thank-you note was the thing to do.

If you didn't, you could expect to be crossed off your host's invitation list.

I ventured to ask Anne if I could see her invitation list. Had she crossed many people off it?

That was a mistake. Anne didn't have a list – and, of course, I knew that.

The next day, Anne found a pretty notelet and filled it with thanks as only she can do.

Maybe I am hopeless, as Anne seems to believe. I would just say, "Thanks, both, for a nice evening." If said with sincerity, I don't think any more is necessary.

Talking of etiquette, did I ever tell you about Anne finding out at a church sale that our son had a girlfriend?

Anne was not best pleased. She didn't know anything about it, but she managed to keep that concealed from the woman who had imparted the news.

She tackled Paul that evening.

"You'll like her, Mum."

That was all Anne could get out of him, much to my amusement. Finally he promised to bring her to meet Anne and me the following week.

I think that week was the longest in Anne's life as she waited and wondered what sort of a girl would appear.

Where had he met her? Did we know her family? How long had this been going on?

But I will skip further details and go straight to the following Sunday, with the sitting-room sparkling and the table groaning with Anne's sandwiches, cakes and scones.

Paul's MG roared into the yard and came to a stop at the back door. He ran around to the passenger side, opened the door and helped Jessie out.

Anne was watching from the kitchen window.

"John Taylor, you never did that for me!" she cried.

She was quite right – I didn't.

But before you agree that I was dragged up, let me say in my defence what I fool I would have looked. I'd have had to get down on one knee, holding her cycle pedal while she dismounted! ■

The More The Marrow-er

I'm never one to turn down a gift of food – especially prize veg!

ANNE saw the smile on my face.

"I just couldn't say no, John."

My smile grew even broader.

It had all started with Anne grumbling to herself – and to me – one evening.

"John, I must go to see Joe and Amy. I feel guilty. I haven't been since Christmas."

Joe and Amy are the salt of the earth, both retired farm workers. They don't have a lot of money, and they spend a lot of their well-earned retirement in their garden.

It's their pride and joy, and produces a lot of entries for the local shows, both flowers and vegetables.

Finally, Anne got round to taking them two pots of her home-made marmalade. It's really tasty – though I might be biased.

It was obvious, Anne said, that if Mrs Taylor had taken the time to come and see them and had brought them a present, she was not going to be allowed to leave empty-handed.

Result – despite Anne's protest – Joe cut her his best marrow.

I have to say that Anne and I are not really marrow fans; we've never got the hang of making the most of them. To be honest, there are plenty other vegetables I would choose to eat before a marrow.

But when she told me the story, I could see her point. How could she have said no?

Well, that marrow sat like the crown jewels in a large willow pattern bowl on the sideboard.

I began to worry that it might be going bad, and neither of us can abide wasting good food. It's the way we were brought up, in the days when nothing was ever wasted. Should I suggest to Anne that she look up a recipe for marrow and ginger jam?

I decided to keep quiet. But it seemed Anne was also concerned about the marrow going to waste, so she looked out a recipe for stuffed marrow.

"John, help me with the marrow, dear."

I could tell by the "dear" that she was worried. We read and reread the recipe.

Peel the marrow. My job. *Cut the marrow in half and take out the seeds*. Easy. But it was the filling I was really interested in.

Anne had mixed together a pound of best minced beef, breadcrumbs, herbs and, as the book instructed, one onion, finely chopped.

Have you noticed how onions seem to disappear when cooked? I peeled and cut up one, then another two! These were added to the breadcrumbs.

Anne also added salt and pepper, plus a beaten egg to bind. Then the mixture was stuffed into the marrow.

At this point, we realised we had a problem. Well, do you have a dish big enough to take a prize marrow?

Finally, we cut a bit off the end and wrapped the stuffed marrow in tin foil. Then, with much pressure, we managed to force it into our roasting tin.

The result was very, very tasty. I'm sure we'll be having it again – if someone gives us another marrow! ■

A Burnt Offering

Our guests will never know how close their meal came to being ruined . . .

ANNE was upstairs getting changed. She'd invited an elderly couple from church to come for a meal.

We were expecting them about half past six. Their son had said he'd bring them. He'd also told me, after church, that his mother wouldn't eat much.

I duly passed the information on to Anne.

She decided to prepare shoulder of lamb on the bone, which was smelling delicious in the oven. She'd also made her own mint sauce, which is out of this world.

"John, put the potatoes and the cauliflower on the stove," Anne called downstairs.

I did exactly what she told me, as any obedient husband would have done. Unfortunately, I didn't do what any house-trained husband would have done!

I put the pans on the stove and went across the yard to put the farm buggy in the shed. I was still tidying up outside when I heard a yell from the back door.

"John!"

I knew by the tone that something was wrong.

And as I approached the back door I could smell something was wrong.

How was I to know Anne hadn't put any water in the cauli? And, of course, guess who got the blame for not checking? I only did what I'd been told – for once! I still maintain she never told me you have to put boiling water on a cauliflower.

Thank goodness the smell hadn't got all over the house.

With great difficulty, we opened the front door.

Our front door is at the back, opening on to the garden, not the yard. We only use it on rare occasions. All the coming and going on the Riggin is through the back door.

The door squeaked open, letting the breeze from the north blow down the passage and out of the back door.

The smell of burned cauliflower went with it, towards Fife Ness and on to Siberia.

Back to the kitchen . . .

Now, Anne always puts a cauliflower wrong end up in the pan. The top of the cauli is at the bottom, so that when she tips it out into a dish, it comes out the right way up.

Simple.

When Anne and I investigated, it was worse than we thought. We found that not only was the top burned, it was well and truly stuck to the pan.

"John, do we have any peas in the deep freeze?" Anne asked in dismay.

I didn't reply. I was concentrating on getting the cauliflower out of the pan and on to a plate.

We didn't need peas. I managed to remove the burnt bits, and cut the cauliflower into florets. When cooked, Anne smothered them with a thick cheese sauce.

"Anne, how do you do your cauliflower?" the dear old lady asked later, as we were sitting round the table enjoying the meal. "The sauce is out of this world. You really must show me how you make it some time."

There are times when it's difficult to keep a straight face . . . ■

Anything You Can Do . . .

I was caught in the middle when Anne refused to be outdone!

THE phone rang at lunchtime and Anne answered it.

"I'd be delighted to see you," I heard her say. "What time will you be coming?

"Maggie's coming over for a blether this afternoon," Anne told me when she came off the phone.

I knew Maggie would have some scandal or other hot news to impart – in secret, of course. That suited me fine. I had no wish to sit and listen politely to women's talk when there was work to be done on the farm!

I didn't say any of this to Anne, of course, but just waited until after milking to discover the reason for the visit.

Well, I was wrong. For once it wasn't scandal but something quite different.

Maggie had come by to bring my Anne a pot of crab-apple jelly.

Anne showed me as soon as I came in the door. It was a beautiful colour, and so clear.

"She obviously knows how to make a good jelly," I told Anne admiringly.

"Oh, it wasn't Maggie who made it – she says her Alistair did," Anne informed me.

I mulled over this remark. Was I being taken to task? But I have been told often enough: "The kitchen is my province – you stick to running the farm!"

To tell you the truth, I'd never dream of making apple jelly even if I could. Give me thick plum jam any time.

However, I said none of this to Anne. I've learned to keep my mouth shut on certain occasions, and this was one.

A few years ago, Anne had planted a crab-apple tree in the garden, and this year the fruit was abundant. I could see the wheels turning in Anne's head.

It soon became clear that if Alistair could make jelly, Anne was determined that her John could, too!

There is no time like the present as far as Anne is concerned. Next day we gathered eight pounds of crab-apples. I'd never have believed there were so many.

The apples were simmering nicely in the pan and when they were done we hung the jelly bag from a peg in the kitchen ceiling and let it drip all night into a big basin.

In the morning, Anne completed the jelly-making process while I looked for jars.

As it boiled hard, Anne skimmed off the top, which was delicious on my morning piece.

The apple pulp that was left went into the sow's feeding trough. Judging by the noise she was making, she really enjoyed getting her snout into those apples.

Anne ended up with fourteen pots of jelly, a beautiful colour and quite firm, as good jelly should be.

I'm not sure how much I contributed to the process, to be honest, but Anne was happy. We gave a few jars away, sent some to a sale of work and kept the rest.

Of course, Maggie and Alistair were sent a pot, just to show that the Taylors could make crab-apple jelly, too! ■

No Bones About It

Too many cooks may spoil the broth, but they certainly improve the hotpot!

ANNE came into the yard in the farm buggy after delivering small bags of potatoes in Crail with a big smile on her face. In fact, she looked as pleased as Punch.

"I've asked Doris and Freda for lunch tomorrow," she explained finally.

"Why, is it their birthdays?"

"Not that I know of. I just felt sorry for them, stuck away there on their own."

"How are they getting here?" I asked.

"They said they'd find their own way here, but I promised to run them home."

Over tea, I asked what she would be giving Freda and Doris for lunch. I'm always interested in talking about food!

Anne hadn't thought about it.

"Oh, there's plenty in the freezer."

After tea, Anne went searching. She found some pieces of stewing steak and some kidney to go with it. We always have plenty of vegetables to hand, so she decided to turn it into an old-fashioned hotpot.

"Would you do some carrots, onions and potatoes, dear?"

That set me thinking about hotpots. It was a long time since Anne had made one, and I do enjoy them.

Granny always made a big one for our Christmas Eve supper, using a big brown jar with a lid. She cooked it very slowly and I can still remember the taste. It was out of this world.

My thoughts were interrupted by Anne.

"Oh, John, you've done far too much for the meat!"

I smiled to myself and began to plan . . .

Anne has a cabin of hens in a field down from the steading that she always likes to see to herself. She's good with poultry and the hens lay well for her.

I was in the byre when she set off to feed them, leaving her meat and vegetables simmering slowly on the stove.

I nipped quickly into the kitchen and took out two beef stock cubes. I put them in a cup with boiling water and added them to the pot.

The stew, and Anne's apple snow and ice-cream, were enjoyed by all.

"John, that must have been better steak than I thought."

I agreed. What else could I say?

You may be wondering where I got the stock cubes from. Anne doesn't believe in them – she always uses bones for soup.

We often have sales of work on Saturday mornings, and I make a point of trying to support them.

The minister and the laird are always pleased to see me. There's usually half a dozen men and about a hundred women!

I never know what to buy at the work and bric-à-brac stalls, so I make my way to the food. You can't go wrong there.

I relieve them of all sorts, but I never buy jam or marmalade. That would be an insult to my Anne.

At the last sale of work, my purchases included some home-made tablet, some fancy cakes – all very fattening – and twelve beef stock cubes.

Let's keep that little story just between ourselves. Please don't tell my Anne that her steak was "better than she thought" because of those! ■

It's The Thought That Counts

I admit I'm less than gifted when it comes to choosing presents for Anne!

WHAT will I get Granny for her birthday? If I've been asked that question once, I've been asked it a hundred times. And it's always a problem . . .

Anne always tells me not to bother, but if I must give her something, to pick something simple.

Even before we were married, I remember wondering what to give her for her birthday.

I was in Cupar and I found myself going into the chemist's, not really knowing what I was looking for.

A comely soul – at least twice my age – came over and said, "Can I help you, sir?"

She was one of those motherly sorts to whom you could tell your problems, so I told her mine.

She smiled and said she had just the thing, and picked out a bottle of 4711 perfume, saying it was the latest and the best. She gift-wrapped it and I left the shop in high spirits.

Anne was as pleased as Punch. No-one had ever bought her perfume before.

By November 1936, Anne and I were engaged – but I still didn't know what to get her for her birthday.

On the Saturday afternoon, I took the buggy to the far-off city of Kirkcaldy. It was only fifteen miles away, but you didn't travel far in those days.

I went into a big ladies' shop – no, that can't be right! You know what I mean! A big shop, selling things for ladies!

I looked around, but I knew I had to be careful. No doubt Anne would say a big thank you for whatever I gave her, but any present had to win her mother's approval, too.

I explained to the lassie, and she smiled and took me across to the dressing-gowns.

She showed me some, but I saw one on her rack which looked better – pink and pleated. I asked her to fetch it down.

The girl gave me the distinct impression that that particular item was more suited to a laird's good lady, not some poor lowly farmer's intended.

I was so annoyed that I told her to wrap it for me. I didn't even ask the price. When she told me, I didn't bat an eyelid – something I'm still very proud of!

Anne is no fool. She realised as soon as I gave her the parcel that it was something special.

And yes, she still has the dressing-gown. It has been much worn and carefully washed, many times.

These days the family usually gives Anne plants, choosing ones which can eventually go outside in the garden.

This year, our eldest grandson had a bright idea. In his local garden centre in Sussex, he had seen a small stone trough with a dwarf conifer growing in it.

Rather than bring it up on the plane, though, he decided to wait and buy one in Scotland – but he couldn't find anything he liked once he got here.

So he gave her a large bottle garden instead.

When he handed it over, he told her about the wee tree, and he was so disappointed about not getting it for her that Anne was nearly in tears for him!

Next time I'm certain if he sees a present for someone, he'll buy it there and then – and worry about transport later! ■

Anne's Victorian Tea

It was almost like going back in time at Anne's tea party . . .

ANNE was sitting in her Orkney chair with a smile on her lips and a twinkle in her eye.

"Penny for them," I said.

"Well, if you really want to know, I'm thinking of giving another Victorian tea," she said.

I remember quite clearly the first time Anne gave a Victorian tea.

It was a beautiful July day, and Anne was washing an exquisite circular tablecloth her mother had given us. When I asked why, Anne told me she was giving a Victorian tea. I was intrigued.

"I'd thought of asking Maud from Buddo and the Misses Riley."

I smiled. The Misses Riley were the perfect people to invite to a Victorian tea. They were real ladies; Janet painted landscapes and Jessie pressed flowers.

They always made things for, and gave generously to, any functions we had in the village.

Maud from Buddo was ten years older than Anne and very suitable to make up the fourth member of the tea party.

What, I wondered, did you serve at a Victorian tea? I was soon to learn. Dainty sandwiches, dropped scones and a sandwich cake.

Sandwiches, cut in wee squares and triangles with no crusts – these were kept for a bread pudding the next day.

And oh, the fillings – cucumber (one round in each), and boiled egg mixed with home-made salad dressing and tomato. The sandwich plate was decorated with sprigs of parsley.

In the centre of the dropped scones was a spot of clear honey. The two sponges were filled with homemade lemon curd.

Well, Janet, Jessie and Maud were all delighted to come at 3.30 p.m. on the appointed day.

The crocheted cloth was draped over the table and a little bunch of flowers had been placed in the centre. Four plates, plus napkins, a silver teapot, a hot water jug, cream and sugar bowls were all artistically positioned.

As I came through to look at Anne's beautifully laid table, I saw a wee silver tray on the oak chest.

"What's this for?" I didn't remember seeing it before.

"Oh, John, you've got your fingerprints all over it! I'll have to repolish it now."

It was, so I was told – you're never too old to learn – a visiting card tray.

"The Misses Riley will leave their cards, John, and there must be a card tray to put them in."

After lunch on the Victorian day, I was told to take logs into the lounge. Despite the fact that it was July, Anne wanted a log fire in the grate.

At 3.35 p.m. – it's fashionable to be five minutes late – the Riley sisters and Maud arrived.

As they entered, Janet produced a small parcel and so did Jessie.

Anne opened the parcels – one was a pound of tin tea from Jackson's of Piccadilly and the other was a small picture of pressed cowslips.

And right enough, as Janet, being the elder, passed through the hall, she dropped their visiting cards in the tray.

From what I gathered, the tea was a great success. The Riley sisters wrote a beautiful letter saying how much they'd enjoyed it.

I'll be honest with you. I was very, very proud of my Anne. She's a real lady, too . . . ■

A lovely day for afternoon tea.

Pause For
Thought

British Is Best!

I believe in supporting home industry – especially where cheese is concerned!

I'VE been worrying about something lately. Anne tells me I can't do anything about it, but I don't agree.

You must have heard how much money this country owes abroad. Britain is very deep in debt – and nobody seems the least bit bothered!

When I hear the amounts of money they talk about as if it were nothing at all, it makes my head spin.

Anne and I are proud to say we don't owe anyone a penny. When we get a bill, it's paid.

In London they seem to ignore the national debt – they call it our balance of payments.

I suppose that sounds better than saying that all the money in this country is owed abroad!

So I worried and worried and finally decided, much to Anne's amusement, what I could do to help.

Now as you know, I like my food, and I have a habit of buying odds and ends just in case Anne runs out of them.

"I've just brought you this, dear," I'll say, when I arrive home with oxtails or tongues.

"John, we don't need it!" she'll say, trying to hide her annoyance – and not often succeeding.

Really, it's a compliment to her cooking. She's very good at making the most of meats. Give Anne a neck of lamb, and back comes a mouth-watering stew.

There's nothing I like better in winter than coming into the warm kitchen – the aroma of a good stew soon makes you forget the cold outside.

And the taste! You wouldn't get a better dish if you went to a posh hotel and paid the earth.

Come to think of it, the last time we went to a posh hotel, I ended up wishing we'd gone into St Andrews for a poke of chips!

It was my birthday, I remember, and Anne had wanted to treat me. I had a meat dish because it said it was served with vegetables.

How Anne laughed. Vegetables! I got six pods – like pea pods without any peas in them – and two wee potatoes!

Oh, the meal was tasty enough but I could have eaten the whole thing again – twice!

I'm afraid I've strayed from my worry about the balance of payments. I'm trying to do my bit to keep it down, so I won't let Anne buy those cheeses with fancy names from across the Channel.

I reckon we in Britain can make as good a cheese as anyone. They're produced from the Orkneys, through nearly every milk-producing county, to the south of England. And it's delicious. So why do we need to buy foreign?

Anne laughs – but I look more carefully to see where a vegetable was grown before buying it.

She also says that if we stopped buying from abroad, they – whoever "they" are – would stop buying from us.

She might be right. I'm no economist or high financier. It just seems to me we've been buying too much from abroad or we wouldn't owe so much.

Have I got it all wrong?

I might have – but I still worry about how we're going to pay off that high debt.

One thing's for sure – the more money we can generate in this country for this country, the stronger we'll be.

Buy British – that's my answer! ■

Saying It With Flowers

Wild blooms can be just as pretty as shop-bought ones, in my humble opinion . . .

THERE had been a wedding in our church on the Saturday, a lassie from outside the village. She wasn't a churchgoer, but had always wanted to be married in white in a pretty wee country church, and ours certainly fitted the bill.

Our minister is very good with young folk. When the bride and her fiancé came to see if he would wed them, he had a wee chat with them and then he agreed.

He hoped, I suppose, that it might lead them and their bairns to church in future.

We in the village would not have known anything about the wedding but for one thing – the flowers!

Now, the flower ladies at the church, of whom my Anne is one, do a great job week after week. I often find myself admiring the pretty arrangements at the altar when I should be attending to the minister's sermon!

But these were stunning. There was a beautiful, tall display of lilies and greenery in the porch. On either side of the altar, flowers rose in a pyramid to the sky.

On each window-ledge there was a basket of flowers and at the side of the first ten seats from the front there were baskets of flowers on the pew-ends.

As Anne remarked, the bride's father must have been out to impress the groom's family. However, I agreed with her that it was rather overdone.

"I bet the young folk could have done with the money he spent on all that."

After the Sunday service, I was discussing the current trade in lambs with John Cameron while Anne was talking to Alice, a local farmhand's wife.

On the way home, Anne told me about Alice's wedding and the flowers she had that day. Alice was a Sunday school teacher, well-loved by everyone in the parish.

She told Anne that there were two vases of flowers in the church for her wedding, and they did not come from any expensive florist – they were wild flowers picked by the local people.

They brought her a bouquet of wild flowers the night before. She put them in water and then wrapped the stalks in silver paper before carrying them to church the next day.

They cost nothing but love, and signified the great respect her neighbours had for Alice.

Anne is a great one for making a display of flowers. At the back-end of one summer, when flowers were scarce and expensive, we went into the hedgerows.

It's surprising what you can find in the country lanes in the way of leaves and dried grasses, and so long as they're the common kind and there are masses of them, picking a few here and there does no harm to anyone. Anne's always very careful to leave plenty for other folk to enjoy.

Anne took her findings home, gave some a wee tint of gold and, in my eyes, ended up with a smashing backdrop of flowers for the church.

As Anne says, God can shine in the hedgerow often better and cheaper than in a florist's.

After all, the flowers are in church for his glorification, not to get one up on all the other flower ladies! ■

A Gift For Anne

I outdid myself that day with two perfect presents for my wife!

I HATE losing things. Anne is even worse. But to give her her due, she doesn't lose much. More often, she puts something safely away and then can't find it.

"I've lost it," she moans.

"Darling, you wouldn't have taken it out of the house, would you? It can't be lost."

"Well, you find it then," she says, in one of those voices.

In St Andrews there was a shop called the Woollen Mill. Anne loved it and could never pass the door.

I was dragged in one day because she wanted to buy a travelling rug. As soon as we were inside Anne disappeared, and I was left to wander round on my own.

There was one counter with lengths of different coloured material. One swatch – I think that's the proper word for it – with a smart blue check design caught my eye. Something made me think that Anne would suit it.

I asked the lassie behind the counter if it would make a skirt.

"How big is the lady?"

I pointed to Anne, who, by this time, had moved over to the sweater counter.

The assistant said it would make a skirt with a bit left over. I paid for it and, without telling Anne, put it in the car boot.

There's a lady in Guardbridge who does dressmaking for Anne. I could ask her to make up the skirt as a surprise without letting Anne into the secret.

She already has all Anne's measurements so all I would have to do was get the material to her – and pay for it afterwards, of course!

I felt very pleased with myself. I always have a job knowing what to get Anne for her birthday and here was the answer!

When I managed to get into Guardbridge next I paid a visit to the dressmaker.

She agreed the material would make a nice skirt and thought there would be enough left over to make a beautiful scarf.

When I called a few weeks later to collect the finished goods, I was absolutely delighted. She had done a smashing job. Anne, on her birthday, was equally happy.

"Let's go out for a meal," Anne suggested.

We went for a lovely bar supper in St Andrews and Anne wore her skirt and scarf. She looked beautiful in them and I was very proud of her.

The following day, Anne was looking worried when I came in at lunchtime.

"John, have you seen my scarf?"

She'd looked all over, so we went out and searched the car, but with no luck.

We tried phoning the the hotel, and even the police, but all to no avail.

Anne was very disappointed, and annoyed at herself for being careless.

Don't say anything, but the next time I'm in St Andrews I'm going to take Anne's skirt into the Woollen Mill and try to get a piece of the same material – regardless of the cost.

Then I'll have a new scarf made up and give it to her, perhaps for Christmas.

I can hear her say, "Oh, John, where did you find it?"

She might even give me a kiss! ■

If You Can Help Somebody

Anne's good turn led to a pleasant evening for the two of us.

ANNE has always been keen on young men. Now don't get me wrong, she could go to the ends of the earth and come back a true and honest wife.

But Anne dotes on boys – you should see the fuss she makes of our grandsons. That's why I'm telling you this story.

Anne had been visiting in Kingsbarns and, as she passed a telephone box, a young man leaned out.

"Please can you assist me?" he asked.

The boy, who was in his early twenties, was camping with his wife near Cambo. He had come into the village to phone his mother in Holland.

Well, the phone box in Kingsbarns is a bit old-fashioned and he had found it difficult to operate.

He had wasted a lot of money already trying to get through, so Anne kindly suggested he came home with her to the Riggin and telephoned from there.

As Anne and the young man arrived in the yard, I was coming from the byre, where I'd been working.

"John, this is – what's your name?"

"Ian."

He shook my hand and told me in perfect English he was pleased to meet me. We went inside and before long he was chatting away in Dutch to his mother.

Ian wanted to pay for the call, and although we told him to forget it, he wouldn't.

He had rung his mother the previous night, and he gave us the same amount of money as that call had cost.

Anne asked about his wife.

"Why not bring her up to meet us tomorrow night?" she suggested.

You could see he was delighted.

When the lad was gone, two questions remained – what should we give them to eat, and what on earth would we find to talk to them about?

Anne made some nice sandwiches and put tomatoes, cucumbers and cheese on cream crackers. And it didn't take her long to knock up some scones and a nice fruit loaf.

What would we talk about, though? I didn't know anything about Ian's country, although Anne and I had once gone on a trip to Holland to see the bulb fields.

On the dot of eight, the laddie and his wife arrived. Her name was Frieda and luckily, her English was as good as Ian's, so we were off to a good start.

We chatted, and they told us where they had been and where they were planning to go next.

We still couldn't remember the places we had visited in Holland, but somehow it didn't matter in the atmosphere of friendliness and laughter their presence created.

We have seldom spent a happier evening and at the end of it, as the young couple took their leave, with promises to stay in touch, we were glad we had had the chance to play hosts to such charming visitors to Scotland. ■

The Case Of The Disappearing Knife

I freely admit my memory's not as sharp as it used to be!

THE older I get, the more I seem to worry about small things. Take my latest concern. It was all about a small knife.

We have a number of useful articles in the kitchen, many from when we were first married.

Looking back, Anne and I smile at some of the presents we received.

Many of the wives near Anne's farm came up with "just a wee minding" and proceeded to stay all afternoon, drinking tea and eating cake.

Well, one of those wee presents was a small kitchen knife, with a four-inch-long blade and a dark-brown handle. It was very sharp. I don't think it cost more than one shilling and threepence.

For the last forty-odd years it has proved itself time and again to be the best present we were ever given. I must have used it to peel bags of potatoes and onions.

I love onions. I like them best when they are boiled, put in a deep dish and covered with a thick white sauce.

Anne's an expert at making white sauce just that bit better by adding a mysterious ingredient.

She's stopped making it for the time being, though. When I asked why, I was told in no uncertain terms that it was for my own good.

"Look at your figure!"

But to come back to our little sharp knife.

I was going to peel an apple before going to bed. I opened the drawer to get the knife, but it wasn't there.

I looked round the kitchen and went into the dairy, but it wasn't there, either.

"John, are you coming to bed tonight?" Anne asked a little impatiently.

"Yes, dear, right this minute." I put the apple back in the fruit bowl and went to join Anne. I got into bed, but I couldn't sleep. I couldn't get that knife out of my head.

"John, did you have cheese before you came to bed?" Anne asked the next morning.

I could say no with a clear conscience. I hadn't had anything, had I?

"Well, you tossed and turned and talked in your sleep."

It suddenly dawned on me that the last time I had seen the knife I had been peeling onions for Anne. I wondered if it had gone into the dustbin with the peelings?

I tipped everything out of the bin, but it wasn't there.

Isn't it silly? I worried all day about that knife. I kept telling myself we could buy another, but we'd had it for forty years.

I didn't offer to peel anything for days, and Anne obviously didn't need it during that time.

Oh, yes, I found it eventually, on the sill in the garage, and I suddenly remembered putting it there. I never told Anne, I just put it back in the drawer.

It would have been so much easier if I could have just put it out of my mind and bought another knife – but Anne and I aren't made that way, and perhaps that's no bad thing! ■

A Good Night's Sleep

Snore? Not me! Well, not unless I eat cheese before bed!

I MET Jack today. He looked quite drawn.

I was a bit worried and so I asked Anne if Jack's wife had said anything about him being ill, but she dismissed my fears.

"He's probably just tired," she said. "They never go to bed until after midnight."

Jack, I suppose, gets up at 6.30 every morning, like me, and like most farmers of my acquaintance. How anyone can survive on six hours' sleep, I can't imagine.

Anne generally goes to bed at half past nine, just after the news. I am never usually far behind. If we're still up at ten o'clock, it's a late night for us.

The other evening, a fellow farmer dropped in just as we were about to hit the hay.

He was on his way home from the local pub and, after making him a sandwich and a black coffee, Anne told me I should probably run him home.

I was quite happy to do it, but it meant I didn't get to bed till after eleven! I made sure I was in bed early the following night to make up the sleep I had lost.

I do like my sleep. Anne says I snore, but I think that's only if I lie on my back and have eaten a cheese sandwich before retiring – which I do whenever I can get away with it.

Anne has tried to get me out of this habit. She now makes a thick oatmeal porridge, which I enjoy with a drop of cream. I think I actually do sleep better after having that for supper than I do after eating cheese.

They say a good bed is important if you want to get a good night's sleep. It mustn't be too soft, apparently. We have a firm bed, but it's a bit too firm for my liking.

Many years ago, we went to a wedding in Kirkby Lonsdale. We stayed in a hotel where the bed was an old-fashioned one with a wire base and feather mattress.

Now that bed was soft.

Anne and I both fell into the middle. However we tried, we couldn't sleep in our own halves.

The next morning, I asked who the owner of the hotel was. I wrote to him and, some time later, when we returned to the same hotel, we were given the Royal Suite.

At home, Anne sleeps on the left side and I sleep on the right. Any time we're away, we have to go through the ritual of standing at the bottom of the bed to work out whose side is whose.

Some nights I fall asleep as soon as my head hits the pillow, but other nights I don't.

I was telling my doctor of a recent night when I heard the grandfather clock chime every hour.

"You're lucky to have a grandfather clock, John. And I'm afraid it's Anno Domini. At your age, you don't need so much sleep, so I'm not giving you sleeping pills."

I wonder if eating a bigger helping of oatmeal porridge would help me to sleep better?

I must ask Anne. ■

The Sound Of Silence

Sometimes you have to kick up a row for some peace and quiet!

WHENEVER something goes wrong – so Anne says – I rush upstairs to my word factory. That's what my granddaughter calls the small single bedroom where I am allowed to have a desk, a few files and some bookcases.

I like my little room. I can sit and think there, and watch what goes on between the farm and the Forth.

It's also where I sit when I write to you to tell you what's happening on the Riggin!

Anyway, I'd come in just before six to listen to the news on the radio. I switched it on and there was hardly a squeak. I moved it about, but it got no better.

It had been all right at six in the morning for the news. What was different now?

I asked Anne. I could tell from her face she knew why. Anne can never tell a lie.

We had had the decorators in and they had taken my radio, without so much as a by your leave, to the room where they were working, and had retuned the station.

Anne said that she had heard it blasting out pop music, but she thought they had brought their own radio – until she went looking for ours!

She says she considered taking it back, but she was afraid they'd be offended and do a second-rate job, so there it stayed until they left at four-thirty.

They didn't even bother turning it off, let alone bring it back downstairs!

Later that week, a mechanic came from Cupar to work on a tractor. Before he even asked me what I thought was wrong, he pulled out a little radio and turned it on, filling the whole shed with the most ludicrous noise.

It was a woman – I was going to say singing – but it sounded more like screaming.

Coming so soon after the episode with the painters, I couldn't help myself. I asked him if he really listened to that noise, or if he just had it on for company. He looked taken aback.

I was told that that particular "tune" was number five in the charts that week. I dreaded to think what number six sounded like!

Going down South Street in St Andrews the other day, I found myself watching a young man with a hairstyle like a man from Mars, carrying a large radio and blasting everyone around him with a force-ten gale of sound.

What is this desire for noise? Are people frightened of solitude? Does silence terrify them?

No doubt if many of you saw Anne and me out for a walk, you would smile. We stroll along arm-in-arm, or – even at our age – holding hands.

We can go for ages without exchanging a word, just happy to be together in such a world of beauty.

I can't abide those women who don't seem to be able to stop, not talking, but eternally chattering.

Which reminds me – I must remember to get new batteries for my wee black box.

Not for any of that pop music, mind you – I prefer to listen to the weather and the news! ■

That's My Anne!

We've been married a long time, but she never ceases to surprise me . . .

I'M proud of Anne. No man could wish for a better partner. She's not only a farmer's wife, who can lend a hand when needed, she's also an excellent homemaker.

I sometime think she rubs and polishes too much – but I shouldn't grumble. There certainly isn't a better cook in the whole of the East Neuk of Fife!

And she has always been, in my eyes at least, beautifully dressed. She takes a pride in her appearance without being vain.

When we were first married I remember us going away from Crail station for a three-day holiday.

On the first day Anne wore a long, yellow dress with black spots. It was six inches off the ground and had a crinkly edge. I remember it distinctly as it was so unusual.

Next day she had a woollen dress with a brown and white triangular pattern.

I thought she looked so pretty, I took a photo of her as we were having a picnic. I only had a Brownie camera, but I was delighted with the result.

It's a lovely shot of my Anne – just head and shoulders, but she's smiling and looks so happy. She's wearing her hair curled into "earphones."

When I first met her, coming home from Cupar show, her hair went all the way down her back, although she didn't wear it that way, of course.

I remember her showing me how she could sit on her hair.

After we started going out together, she put her hair up into earphones.

Unfortunately, this affected her ears a bit, but her father forbade her to get her hair cut. In fact, she didn't get it cut until we'd been married for quite a while.

Anne was left a bow-fronted chest of drawers in the will of a maiden aunt who lived in St Andrews.

It's a beautiful piece of furniture and she had a piece of plate glass cut to fit the top to protect it.

I don't know what you do with your family snaps. Do you put them in an album and hardly ever see them, because the album is put away tidily?

We have several albums which just sit in the sideboard. We also have a wee case full of old photos, some of them going back to my grandparents' day.

When we do take the time to look at them, we always enjoy it, and it brings back so many memories of happy times and people who are no longer with us.

But for the most part, all our photos stay shut in the sideboard and never see the light of day.

When Anne had her idea, I thought it was a brainwave.

She wanted us to look at our favourite pictures whenever we wanted to. So under the plate of glass on the chest of drawers she arranged twenty-four photographs.

There are pictures of our children at various ages, and our grandchildren.

Some wedding groups, too, and one of Anne's dad with a big Clydesdale horse.

There's even one of me, aged seven or so, on the back of a horse. Where she got that one, I don't know!

But my favourite is the one I took of Anne. Head and shoulders, in her brown and white wool dress, laughing into the camera, taken just after we were married.

And she looks just as bonnie today as she did then. ■

John and Anne enjoy an evening stroll.

In Anne's Kitchen

Five A Day?

You don't need to worry about counting five portions when I go shopping!

ANNE says I do daft things on the spur of the moment. She always says that in the old days I would have been called eccentric or odd. Well, I don't agree. I don't think I'm either. I just like to enjoy life.

The other day, Anne sent me into Cupar. She gave me a long shopping list which included three pounds of apples. We were having visitors and she was making an apple pie.

It was a nice day and I enjoyed the drive. I found somewhere to park the buggy and had a stroll round the shops.

I couldn't be doing with living in town. I would call myself a sociable fellow, but there are just too many people. However, it's fine for a visit now and then.

Eventually I went into the fruit shop in Cupar for Anne's apples. I decided to add four bananas to the list.

Then I found myself thinking of a picture I particularly like in one of Anne's cookery books – three big boiled onions on a plate, covered with thick parsley sauce . . .

I bought four pounds of onions. You should never be without onions, and I love them.

I also bought a grapefruit. Well, I'm always being told I'm overweight, and I believe grapefruit is a good thing to eat if you're slimming.

Anne splits them, sprinkles each half with brown sugar and slips them under the grill. Beautiful.

Cauliflowers were cheap. I felt sorry for the grower, knowing how much he got for each one.

I bought one just the same, because Anne's cauliflower cheese is out of this world. She puts a wee pinch of mustard in the sauce, and it makes all the difference.

I was enjoying myself, browsing round that fruit shop. Anne says I'm always happy anywhere there's food!

Then I saw a pineapple and I decided on the spur of the moment that I was going to take it home.

Why did I buy it? Well, I wanted to help Anne with the dinner she was planning for the following Sunday – and I had recalled another picture.

It was in the same cookery book – a bit of a favourite of mine. A pineapple was cut in half and then filled with fresh fruit. It looked mouth-watering.

Well, I paid for my purchases and the lassie behind the counter gave me a box to take them home in.

I set it carefully on the seat beside me in the buggy and set off for the Riggin.

Anne looked a bit bemused when I came in the door carrying, as she put it, "half a greengrocer's shop".

But when I explained what everything was for, I think she appreciated the thought behind it.

On the Sunday, we sat down to celery soup and roast beef with all the trimmings.

I enjoyed it, and I was looking forward to seeing what would be offered for afters.

Anne didn't serve the pineapple as in the picture. Instead, she used part of it, plus pears and grapes and all sorts of other things, for an enormous fruit salad.

It was greatly enjoyed by us all. There were no leftovers for Monday. Pity . . . ■

Using Your Loaf

I don't mind if you call me a crusty old man. I love my bread!

YES, we'll be delighted." Anne spoke into the telephone without looking at me. I noted that I had been included in that "we" – I also noted that I hadn't been consulted on whatever it was she was agreeing to.

"That was our Mary," Anne said, when she eventually put the phone down.

I guessed that. It had been a twenty-minute phone call!

Apparently, Mary had wondered if we'd like to spend a few days with her. Anne knew that things were slack at the Riggin and had agreed. So off we went to the Upper Tay Valley.

I enjoyed getting out and about during the day, delighted at the chance to look over other farmers' fences. But in the evenings, I'm afraid, time hung heavy on my hands.

I was looking through their library for something to read, and I picked up an Agatha Christie.

I hadn't read one for ages, but I didn't get very far this time. Something had caught my attention.

"Listen, dear."

Anne lifted her head from the letter she was writing while I read a bit of the story to her. Miss Marple was being offered some bread and butter pudding.

"I'll make one tomorrow," Anne said.

How we laughed.

Anne and I were brought up not to waste anything. If there was any stale bread left, the answer was a bread pudding.

Anne's are out of this world. Slices of bread, buttered, jam or dried fruit added, then milk and egg, and it's all cooked slowly in a dish in the oven.

After we were married, Anne always made our own bread.

I used to come in for my breakfast about nine o'clock and there would be a big earthenware bowl in front of the stove, covered with a cloth.

It was the bread rising. That was real bread – delicious – and it kept for a week.

Anne only gave up baking her own when the family left home. We buy our bread now, a rough brown because it's good for us, and we have sixteen loaves delivered at a time. We freeze fifteen of them to use as we need to.

It's not so long ago that we ate a loaf a day, but I'm always being urged to eat less, so I've cut out bread. They say it's not good for the waistline.

A pity, because I like a toasted slice with lashings of butter and cheese.

While we were chatting about bread, Anne reminded me of the day she asked me to buy her two ounces of yeast.

"Can I help you, sir?" the young lassie at the shop asked when I went in.

"Two ounces of barm, please."

The lassie looked at me blankly. An old soul behind me said, "The gentleman wants two ounces of yeast."

Someone should have told me they'd changed the name since I went shopping for Granny!

If I asked for yeast today, I wonder what I'd get? Another blank look, no doubt!

I'm not likely to find out, though.

Anne says she's not starting to make her own bread again. It's a pity – but I don't blame her. ■

A Sticky Situation

Not only did I pay for the ingredients, but I had to help with the cooking, too!

I WAS just leaving to go to Cupar when Anne asked me to see if the greengrocer had any marmalade oranges, and if they had, to buy fifteen pounds.

So after a visit to the market to look at bullocks, I ambled up to the greengrocer's.

"Oh, Mr Taylor, your wife's been on the phone. She wants you to bring fifteen pounds of Seville oranges, six lemons and two grapefruit – and you have to buy jam covers and twenty pounds of jamming sugar."

Would you believe it? Once I'd done all Anne's shopping I was seriously out of pocket – and she hadn't given me a penny.

I complained about it when I got home, only to be told, "Well, you do like marmalade, John."

We went to Kingsbarns church on the Sunday and came home to mince, tatties, carrots and onions – all done in one saucepan and left on the stove whilst we were at church – followed by a sponge pudding and lashings of custard.

I was very happy to eat it, of course, but I admit I was a bit suspicious.

Anne doesn't do us that well most Sundays, so I thought there must be some reason why she was feeding the brute.

We were just finishing washing up and I was looking forward to sitting down with my "Farmer's Weekly", when Anne's voice broke into my thoughts.

"John, dear, would you help me with the marmalade?"

So that was the answer.

"Darling, you can't make marmalade on a Sunday – your mother would turn in her grave."

This did not, of course, put Anne off.

My job was to cut up the oranges and take out the pips. I never knew oranges had so many! No wonder Anne didn't want to do it. It took me all afternoon.

Anne took down an ancient recipe book which had belonged to an aunt of mine and must have been over one hundred years old – and looked it.

Soon, three jelly pans were boiling away on the stove.

Let cool, weigh again, and to each pound of fruit add one pound of sugar, the book said.

We weighed the fruit – that was the easy part.

Problem – each sugar packet was in kilos. This made our calculations difficult.

We boiled and boiled. The whole place smelled of marmalade and the walls dripped with steam.

"Let's risk it setting," Anne said at last. I gratefully agreed. It was half-past ten!

Jam jars – how many would we need? Anne's a careful soul and keeps all her empty ones, but we had three full jelly pans bubbling away.

In the event, we ended up with sixty-two pots of marmalade.

I dread to think what the total cost was per jar – especially when half of it found its way to sales of work!

Anyway, at least Anne was happy when we finally went to bed at half-past one in the morning knowing it was a job well done – her year's marmalade was all in jars! ■

Trotting Out An Old Favourite

When Anne calls me an "offal" man, I take it as a compliment!

WE'VE just had pigs' trotters for tea, and for a very special reason – all because of something that happened over fifty years ago . . .

I was in Cupar on Tuesday, looking in the butcher's window, when I saw four pigs' trotters in a tray.

Something came over me. I remembered one of Anne's stories, which I have heard so often I can repeat it word for word. I went into the shop.

"I'll relieve you of your trotters, Janet," I said to the lassie who runs the shop.

"John, there's nothing on these trotters," she replied. "You'll be wanting something else if it's for Anne."

So I bought an ox tongue, an ox tail, three lambs' kidneys for frying and three-quarters of a pound of lambs' liver.

I look forward to the summertime, when Anne serves her home-pressed tongue with salad.

But I knew she'd ask why I had bought this one, and I decided to say it was for David.

He's our youngest grandson, and when he comes to visit, he always asks, "Granny, is it one of your tongues for tea?"

He loves Granny's home-cooked tongue – so naturally Anne always tries to oblige.

You'd laugh if you saw our tongue-pressing arrangement.

The tongue, once cooked and skinned, is put into a small bowl. A plate is then placed on top, followed by the very heavy last Dad used to sole our shoes on.

I believe these days you can buy a machine to press tongues in. I wish I'd remembered that last Christmas, because I never know what to buy her!

When I got back to the Riggin and handed the trotters to Anne, how she laughed!

When Anne and I were young, farmers all kept a pig for their own use.

There were no deep freezes in those days, so when a pig was killed, we sent pieces of pork to the farms round about.

When they killed their pigs, they reciprocated. That ensured a supply of fresh meat over several weeks. It really was a very sensible arrangement.

Anne remembers a time when she was eleven or twelve, being sent to bed after a pig killing.

She says she clearly recalls lying there, imagining how much they were enjoying the trotters downstairs.

In fact, she envied them so much she told me that story at least once a year!

Until I took those trotters in for tea . . .

"To think I've borne my poor mother a grudge all these years – for these!"

I agreed with the butcher that there wasn't much meat on the trotters.

But my Anne can be relied upon to make a delicious meal out of anything. With lots of vegetables, those wee trotters made very good soup! ■

Bad Luck, Old Fruit

Memories of Granny's fruit pudding landed me in a sticky situation!

ANNE'S always remarking how young policemen look nowadays. That's a sign we're getting on in years, or so I always like to tell her.

Another sign is how fast berry-picking comes around – far too fast for my liking.

One evening, Anne was on the phone, and she looked across to the table where I was having my tea.

"Yes, dear. Dad will be delighted to do that."

Quarter of an hour later, she came back to join me.

"That was Mary," she announced.

As if I hadn't worked that out!

"If she hadn't rung, I'd have missed the berries this year," Anne went on.

"And what will I be delighted to do?" I enquired suspiciously.

"Mary wants twelve pounds of gooseberries. I said you'd top and tail them for her."

That summer had been one of the wettest I can remember, and that can spell disaster for the fruit growers.

The first fine day, though, Anne and I headed for a fruit farm near the village of Balmullo.

I'd insisted that Anne phone in her order for ready-picked berries.

It may cost a bit more, but it's money well spent, in my opinion. I'm afraid I'm far past the age of grovelling about on my hands and knees in muddy dreels!

The folk had been very obliging when Anne had called. They'd agreed to have twelve pounds of gooseberries for Mrs Taylor by the evening.

We arrived at six o'clock and right enough, the berries were waiting in a big basket.

Anne paid for them and she decided to take a punnet of rasps and one of strawberries for the next day.

We'd just got into the buggy when she said, "John, go back for some gooseberries for us."

I was happy to! Anne says I can't resist anything to eat.

I went back and bought four punnets of gooseberries, some more rasps for freezing and, on the spur of the moment, two punnets of redcurrants.

Why? Well, it was down to a distant memory from over fifty years ago coming to the fore.

Granny's bread fruit pudding!

I haven't seen a punnet of redcurrants for years and the sight must have just triggered that memory. Isn't it a funny thing the way the mind works? I think so, anyway.

I remember Granny had a blue and white basin which she lined with white bread, then put all sorts of soft fruit in the middle.

A bread top was then covered with a big plate and well weighted down.

Eaten along with one of her egg custards, it was out of this world.

Anne laughed when I came back to the car.

"You'll shred them, John Taylor," she said.

I did, but, oh, boy, what a job! What a weary, sticky job! Never again, not even for Granny's fruit pudding.

And by the way – I still had to top and tail Mary's gooseberries into the bargain! ■

Making A Meal Of It

My Anne can make a marvellous dinner out of almost anything!

DARE I, I thought? What I meant was, dare I risk the wrath of my Anne? It was a wet evening and I couldn't go for a wander up the fields to enjoy the view over the Forth, so I thought I would make a list of what was in the big deep freeze in the dairy.

I tried to work out if there was anything vital missing. Anne would say that all I think about is eating. Well, to me there is nothing wrong with being prepared for tomorrow – and the day after.

Anne is very forward looking. If some relation rings up to say they're coming for a few days, Anne plans every meal long before they have packed their bags.

So, in the freezer, just in case, she had a steak and kidney pie, bacon and egg pie, mince and tattie pie, lots and lots of fruit pies – all labelled so there could be no mistake.

I also found carrots ready cut up, cauliflowers and even new potatoes, blanched and ready for the pan. There was a cooked roast of silverside, a piece of cooked lamb and a cooked chicken – all just in case someone dropped in.

Well, to come back to "Dare I?" – I found, at the bottom of the freezer, a goodly sized leg of pork. How long had we had it? Since we went to that wedding in Kirkby Lonsdale.

I remember going to a real pork butcher in Lancaster who only sold the product of a pig, but, oh, how they turned the humble pig into all manner of tasty bits.

So, I dared – then Anne came into the dairy to see how I was getting on.

"Darling, I think it's time we ate this," I said, tremulously holding up my find.

Anne just laughed. She must have got out of the right side of bed that morning.

"Keep it out, then, and we'll have it hot on Sunday and cold for the rest of the week."

Anne cooked it slowly and it didn't shrink. It was as fresh as the day it was put in the deep freeze. Oh, we had it hot on Sunday with all the trimmings. Monday, Tuesday, Wednesday – cold with salads. Anne can really vary salads – eggs, peppers, grated carrots, lettuce, cold new potatoes, etc.

I had to smile. Anne is a most economical person. She left enough meat on the bone to make a hotpot for Thursday. Bone, meat, carrots, onions, potatoes and some rice. It was a fitting end to a fine piece of pork.

I must admit I enjoy Anne's cold meat, whether it's beef, lamb or pork. I'm lucky Anne was taught to cook by her mother who, if she were alive today, would be appalled at all those ready-made packet meals. The nearest she ever got to buying something in a packet was a half a hundredweight of flour in a cotton bag. The same bag was washed and used to make pillows.

Changed days. Anne's mum wouldn't have had a deep freezer either – which would have been an awful waste of a mouth-watering leg of pork. ■

An Overnight Success

Ever since I was a laddie I've considered the humble mushroom Nature's bounty . . .

NEITHER Anne nor I can resist a bargain. We are careful with our money – that is something we agree on. But where we often fall out is over whether we really need the bargain or not! According to Anne, mine are usually unnecessary, but hers are always just what we wanted.

I have learned it's not worth arguing. But it hasn't stopped me snapping up my bargains whenever I get the chance!

Recently, I was in St Andrews on business and, as usual, I had a job to find a place to park the car.

Finally I found a space, and, as luck would have it, it was right outside a greengrocer's shop.

Anne will tell you that I can never resist looking round a shop that sells food.

I went in for some lettuce and came out with a box of all sorts of things.

I love Anne's hotpots and you can't make a hotpot without onions and carrots, can you? I also bought some small onions and beetroot for pickling.

In an effort to keep my weight down, Anne has stopped making so many puddings and we often have a fruit salad instead. So I bought bananas, apples and oranges.

I was wondering if Anne would let me have some ice-cream with it when I saw the mushrooms – a big box of them.

I've always been partial to mushrooms.

As a laddie, I used to get up about five o'clock in the morning and go out and pick the mushrooms which had sprung up overnight in the fields.

There were no mushroom farmers in those days, and I used to sell the ones I'd gathered.

I only got a few pence for my efforts but I thought myself quite well off!

I recently found myself reading one of Anne's magazines because it contained some recipes which used mushrooms in lots of interesting new ways.

My mouth was watering just reading about them.

At the bottom of the page was a coupon to fill in and I sent away for a whole book of mushroom recipes.

"One of the boys sending for things in my name again," Anne commented when it arrived.

I didn't let on that it was me who had sent for it.

I just read it and, amongst other things, I learned that mushrooms could be frozen.

So I knew I was quite safe buying those two pounds of mushrooms that day.

Anne laughed when she saw them, but she didn't offer to help me peel them.

That evening I found out why. I discovered that there are a lot of mushrooms in two pounds! It took me much longer than I had thought it would.

Still, it's done now, and it's nice to know they're there in the freezer to be fried or popped in a stew whenever we fancy.

Maybe Anne will make a real mouthwatering meal of mushrooms on toast for tea . . . ■

Easy Pickings

We went out for a few brambles and came back with a whole lot of memories . . .

JOHN, I've a desire to . . ."

If Anne had been thirty years younger, I'd have been worried. But at her age – and mine – I was more intrigued. She doesn't often break out with a desire!

I do. And usually Anne disagrees.

"Let's have some lamb chops or frying steak tonight, dear," I'll say hopefully.

"John, you're having two boiled eggs," she'll tell me. "Look at yourself in the mirror."

We were returning from Cupar on a Tuesday afternoon. Anne had been shopping. I'd been to my bank.

We came back via Dunino, as Anne wanted to drop a jar of jam off to a farmer there.

He's a widower now, but his wife used to play bridge with Anne and two other farmers' wives.

They used to go to each other's houses every fourth week. Whether they played bridge, or just chatted over a good farmhouse tea, I don't know.

I do know they enjoyed themselves and Anne always came back with the latest gossip.

The first time I heard Anne say, "I've a desire to . . ." was when she was expecting our first born. It was August, and she wanted strawberries one hot afternoon – which is why I wasn't too worried now!

As we'd come over the top of the Riggin, we'd passed a family out picking brambles.

"John, let's pick some brambles."

"Are you feeling well, dear?"

"It'll be like old times – do you remember?"

It's surprising what you'll do when you're courting. We both smiled as we remembered that evening we went out picking brambles near Largoward . . .

So we went on home and found ourselves a plastic bucket. I looked out my shepherd's crook – marvellous for bringing awkward branches within reach.

We soon found a lane which looked promising. Anne went one way and I the other.

Unfortunately Anne chose the side with a deep ditch that was so overgrown she didn't see it.

She stepped forward to grasp some lovely, big, juicy berries and down she went. Thank goodness the ditch was dry.

She said she shouted, but I'm a bit deaf these days and didn't hear. Eventually she got out by clutching at anything she could on the bank to pull herself up.

"I wonder if anyone saw me? They'd think I was drunk."

I had to smile. Everyone knows Anne doesn't drink.

Before we set out we'd decided we only wanted enough for a bramble and apple pie.

We ended up with enough berries, I should think, to make at least twenty bramble and apple pies!

Anne started to make jam and then discovered she didn't have enough jars!

Luckily, the charity shops in St Andrews were more than helpful, and soon our jam shelf was full.

So, with one thing and another, Anne and I won't forget that September evening in a hurry . . . ■

In A Right Pickle

I couldn't help seeing red when Anne found fault with my cabbage!

AS I was coming through St Andrews one Saturday, I decided to call on my friendly greengrocer.

I like fruit and I'm told it's very good for me, so I use that as an excuse to eat as much as I like.

Well, while I was there, I also bought a lettuce, celery and a red cabbage. It was what they call impulse buying.

I enjoy cold meat and pickle. Anne says I'd pickle anything. Why not? I even wrote away once for a book on pickling.

It dealt with cold pickling, hot pickling, sweet pickles and chutney. I found it very interesting. To my mind, a little bit of pickle with your meal just adds a certain something.

But getting back to my impulse buys.

Anne and I don't see eye to eye on everything – cheese sandwiches at suppertime is a perfect example! – but we are both alike in one respect.

We believe there is no time like the present when we get an urge to do something.

As soon as I got home I began chopping the red cabbage. Then in came Her Highness.

"John Taylor, why on earth would you start pickling on a Saturday night?"

"As we aren't going out anywhere, it's as good as any other night," I countered.

Anne always has an answer.

"Couldn't you have left it till another night and sat and read the paper?"

I told her I wouldn't be long. Sometimes there's no point in arguing. I proceeded to cut the red cabbage into strips before covering it with salt and leaving it for twenty-four hours or so.

The next day I'd rinse off the salt, put the cabbage in jars and cover it with malt vinegar.

I thought about labelling the jars, but you really only have to do that if you're sending it to church sales.

Thinking about church sales – we seem to have had one every other week recently.

One afternoon quite recently, on a Saturday, the church held a marmalade sale. Everyone had to bring a pot or two and the proceeds went to church funds. Anne's an expert at making it, so this was right up her street.

I'm always interested in stalls selling things to eat, especially cakes. I'm afraid I bought too many, but as I pointed out, Anne could always put them in the freezer or give them to Mary or the grandchildren when they called.

Not that I expected to have any left over, mind you. I enjoy something sweet with my cup of tea.

And what, I ask you, was the point of me carting coals to Newcastle in the form of marmalade back to the Riggin when we already have a cupboard full?

Made, as I recall, on a Sunday night, when I wanted to read or watch TV.

That was different, Anne said. The marmalade was a necessity – red cabbage is a luxury.

If you ask me, women just twist everything around to suit themselves! ■

There's no recipe Anne can't master.

Christmas On The Riggin

Reading Between The Lines

One special Christmas gift still influences me to this day.

ANNE and I were chatting the other evening when we got round to discussing the question of newspapers.

Neither of us had been allowed to read a paper on a Sunday – that was absolutely forbidden.

Things weren't much better during the rest of the week, either. Both our families had impressed upon us that there was so much physical work to do on a farm that it was nearly a crime to sit down and read a book.

I think I was eight when I found, in my stocking on the brass bedpost on Christmas morning, the book "Robin Hood".

I read it and reread it again and again. I lived in Sherwood Forest with Robin, Friar Tuck and the outlaws.

Dad even helped me to make a bow and arrow. It was my pride and joy.

Whoever added that book to my stocking unwittingly introduced me to the beauty of the written word. I have been fond of reading ever since.

Anne says that if I get my nose into a book, she's better off talking to the dog . . . it takes more notice.

Well, on this occasion, Anne and I were sitting round the stove – I was reading a farming magazine and Anne was reading the weekly paper.

She works on the principle that if you have paid for a paper you should read every word to really get your money's worth.

She starts on the back page and reads it methodically through to the front. She has one of those habits of reading aloud, particularly when I'm trying to absorb something about fertilisers and crops.

"John, listen to this. If I could get hold of the blighters I'd knock them into shape!"

It was a report on the cost of repairing property damaged by vandals, mostly teenagers. It was over £100,000 for the month.

What a waste of money.

We sat and discussed it.

We came to the conclusion that, in our humble opinion, the teenage troubles of today could be caused by them not knowing how to profitably spend their leisure time.

Perhaps if they had been able – or taught – at an early age to appreciate the wealth of entertainment and enjoyment that can be found between the covers of a book, things might be very different.

So, if you are wondering what to buy your children, grandchildren or a friend's child for Christmas, my suggestion is that you get them a book – a good book with a hero they will wish to follow to the last page.

This may, as my Robin Hood did for me, encourage them to read and lead them to discover some of the delights to be found in literature. I do hope so. ■

The Sentiment That Counts

An old pair of gloves reminded me of Christmas shopping long ago.

I CAME in for lunch last week to find a pair of gloves lying on the table. Anne had been looking for something and had come across them.

"Remember these, John?"

I smiled. I remembered them all too well.

One Christmas, many years ago, Anne had decided to go to Edinburgh to do her Christmas shopping for the family. That particular year she said she knew what I needed.

A few weeks previously we had been at a funeral in Anstruther. It was unbelievably cold. The wind was coming off the water and it was bitter.

My hands were frozen and I was blowing on them to try to warm them.

"I'll buy you some gloves for Christmas," Anne suggested. At that particular moment it sounded like a great idea!

And so Forsyths was a must on our visit to Edinburgh.

A doorman in full regalia opened the door; a gentleman in tails stood within.

"Can I help you, madam?" he asked.

We were taken to the glove department and introduced to the lady whose sole occupation was to serve you with gloves.

There were certainly plenty to choose from, and none of them cheap.

Anne chose a pair of fine pigskin gloves and duly paid.

I was presented with them after Christmas dinner when we opened our parcels.

There were some humorous remarks from the family.

"Dad, you'll have to remember to take them off to milk."

"Those are only for lairds, Dad, not lowly tenant farmers . . ." And so on.

The following March I was invited to a fox drive near Peat Inn. It was a bitterly cold day and I pushed my new gloves into my coat pocket.

When I got back to the Riggin I found, to my dismay, that I had only one glove.

Panic stations!

Without saying a word to Anne, next day I disappeared in the farm buggy to Peat Inn.

It was like looking for a needle in a haystack, and I didn't find the glove.

Next time I was in Edinburgh on my own I took the glove I still had and went to see the glove lady in Forsyths. She suggested, as I only needed one glove, she would order one only. That was service, if you like!

I duly warned Charlie, our postman, that if he saw an envelope from Forsyth's, he was to hand it to me in the yard and not put it with the mail on the kitchen slab.

When the parcel finally came, I put the new glove away in the drawer with the other.

Some time later, at another funeral, it was a very cold day, so I wore my gloves.

I took them off in church and put them on the pew. Trust Anne: she picked them up and noticed they were not the same colour.

When we got back to the Riggin, I had to tell her the story. Give Anne her due, she laughed at my tale but told me off for taking my gloves to a fox drive.

To this day they're still not a true pair in colour, but does it really matter as long as they keep my hands warm? ■

In The Spirit Of Christmas

I don't write letters, but I like to be involved with sending out the Christmas cards!

ANNE is the letter writer in our family. Where she learned the art, I'll never know! It certainly wasn't at school, as she had to leave hers early to help her mother with the family.

I've never known anyone who can pick the right words for the right occasion as she can.

She was the family scribe at home before she was married. Her family even expected her to carry on the tradition after she became my wife!

I will always remember her younger brother ringing us up one night. Billy, like me, wasn't one for using the phone for chit-chat, so I suspected he had an ulterior motive.

I was right.

Anne was out, but he was calling to tell her some farmer had died. Would I ask her if she could write on behalf of the family to the widow to say how sorry they were?

I listened and was amazed.

"Billy," I said, "why don't you do it yourself?"

He put down the phone.

I told Anne when she came back. I thought she was going to tell me off, but she laughed.

"John, you know I'll do it."

Typical Anne, she did! Old habits die hard. I'm sure she gave her brother a phone call to get all the details when I was away in our top fields.

One year, our son, Paul, during his Christmas holidays from university, got a seasonal job with the post office. He ended up working as our village postman.

He told us an old man came to meet him every day, hoping for a card from his daughter.

It never came, and Paul had no other card to deliver. He said he could have wept for the old man, such a pathetic picture, waiting there in hope.

Anne keeps a list of Christmas cards she has sent, and threatens each year to cut it down by half. But she never does. If anything, that list seems to get longer as the years go by.

"We mustn't forget the McAndrews, dear. They sent us a nice card last year."

In my opinion, it would be more in the spirit of Christmas if we all took the time to sit down and think of some of the old folk we know at this busy time of year.

Many will be living at home, some in sheltered housing or in an old folks' home, but how many would welcome a card to stand up in their bedroom?

They'd be pleased and feel they had not been forgotten. And surely that's more in the Christmas spirit than sending one to the McAndrews – all because they sent us one last year?

It's very easy to get caught up in the shopping, cooking, writing and posting of cards and all the socialising that goes on at this time of year – if you're lucky enough to have family and friends to socialise with, that is.

Do you know anyone in hospital who would welcome a card? If so, why not send one?

And don't forget to put your address on the card! It might give them pleasure to send you one, or at least get in touch to say thank you for brightening their Christmas . . .

Fowl Play!

Anne thought I was a bit of a goose when I demanded a duck for my New Year dinner.

A COUPLE came to visit us between Christmas and New Year. The conversation got round to what we were doing for New Year. Anne explained that our son, his wife and the family were coming to spend the day.

"I suppose, Anne, you'll be killing the fatted calf," Jessie said with a smile.

"Well, I did buy a sirloin of beef," Anne replied, "but the old man (that's me) has been harping on about having a duck for ages, so I bought one just to keep him quiet."

"John, how many are coming to lunch?" Jessie's husband, Frank, asked.

"Four," I told him.

"For goodness' sake!" he exclaimed. "A duck will never stretch for six people! If you give your guests a fair helping, there'll be nothing left for you and Anne!"

Cheerful sort, Frank.

Give Anne her due, she is someone who always keeps her word. She had made it quite clear she wasn't keen on having the duck, but if we had to have it to keep "the old man" quiet, she was going to do her very best with it.

We have lots of recipe books. Anne looked through several for a suitable recipe, and one of them told us that you stuff a duck with prunes and apples.

Anne insists that she told me – although I don't remember hearing – to put the prunes to soak the night before.

Sharp words were directed my way on New Year's morning, when prunes went into the duck unsoaked – plus stones.

A lump of sausage stuffing, sage and onion and chestnut stuff went inside that duck, too.

It was a big duck and Anne had difficulty getting it into our roasting tin and getting the lid on.

Later, I was peeling potatoes.

"Anne, your duck is sizzling hard," I told her.

It smelled wonderful, too. I could only hope that Frank was wrong

and that there would be enough for everyone!
The duck was duly put in the bottom of the oven for a bit.
After a while, Anne checked to see how it was getting on.
"John, come here!" she said.
I had never seen so much fat in my life.
Anne, being a very careful sort, said she had enough duck fat to keep her going for the next year.
I asked what she would use it for. She looked at me as though I was daft.
"Pies, sausage rolls and things."
I told her I would like to spread it on bread, but that, she informed me, was not on.
"Won't you ever make an effort to get your weight down?" she asked in despair.
Well, the duck was cooked beautifully. Despite Frank's gloomy predictions, it was ample for six – and three had second helpings!
I stripped the carcass afterwards and we even used the bones for stock.
Anne is just coming out of the dairy eating a duck sandwich, and by the look on her face, she is relishing it.
Despite herself, she has thoroughly enjoyed the duck she claims she bought just to keep me quiet!
Sometimes "the old man" is right – but she won't admit it! ■

Cards On The Table

One minute I was thinking ahead – then I was thinking back . . .

A LOT of people would say that I had wasted the evening being a sentimental old fool. Well, I couldn't care less!

Anne says that's one of my problems, but I rose above that comment. Sometimes, when she makes remarks like that, I refuse to rise to the bait, just to annoy her.

But when I do rise to it, we end up arguing – loudly – and parting company for the next hour or so. Usually only until the next mealtime, if I'm honest.

But I think all couples must go through the same thing. Not so long ago, when we were at a church sale, Anne got chatting with a couple of other ladies that she hadn't seen for a while.

One remarked that her husband had been dead now for over ten years.

"I'll sell you mine," Anne offered.

They all laughed.

"No, lassie," the lady went on. "You keep him. I've had one. That was enough."

The three women laughed even harder.

I've wandered again, haven't I?

All right – why was I a sentimental old fool?

One day quite recently, we were in St Andrews. Anne wanted to find a nice get-well card for an old soul who had been taken into hospital that same week.

She's good at this "cheer-you-up" business with letters and cards. She always says it doesn't cost much in terms of time or money, but the gesture is worth a lot to someone on their own.

There was a new card shop which had just opened, so I went in with her, just to see what they had. I came across a bin with packets of Christmas cards.

They were very reasonably priced, so I chose two packs and paid my money. Anne remarked that I was very well prepared.

I have a small chest of drawers in my office, and I had stored some left-over Christmas cards there last year. I added the new ones to the drawer.

I found far more cards than I remembered, so I sat at my work table to look at them. They were all birthday cards to me from the family.

Have a happy birthday, Grandad. Love, Adam – in very young, squiggly handwriting, but so sincere.

A sedate one from our only granddaughter. On closer examination, I realised she'd chosen it for the wording.

A threshing scene from daughter and family.

One from Anne with a boat on it – again, picked for the verse.

I've gone through them all twice. But I still can't decide what to do with them.

I can't throw them all away, can I? Consign all that thoughtful affection to the wastepaper bin?

So I'll put the rubber band around them again and put them back in the chest of drawers.

I suppose it's true – I am a sentimental old fool. But at least the family know when they send me a card that it is going to be appreciated. ■

The Christmas Visitor

This was one occasion when I had no ready answer for Anne!

"THANK goodness Christmas comes only once a year," Anne said meaningfully as she flopped in a chair by the stove. It was 11.30 p.m. – two hours past our normal bedtime.

We were going to be having the family for Christmas dinner. Our daughter, her husband and the boys – all with large appetites.

Anne had made French onion soup, the boys' favourite, and it would be followed by turkey with all the trimmings and vegetables galore.

For dessert, there would be a choice of Christmas pudding made by Anne, apple pie and lemon meringue pie.

My traditional contribution is to prepare the vegetables and lay the table.

"Don't forget the serviettes, John," Anne reminded me.

Anne maintains the children of today are not taught to use serviettes. Anne's parents were sticklers for table manners, a social grace often sadly lacking these days, I'm afraid.

We were enjoying a few minutes' breather when Anne spoke up.

"I wonder what happened to Fleck?"

I should explain that Fleck – though I doubt that was his real name – was a "gentleman of the road".

Anne knew him better than I did as, on his journey between Anstruther and Cupar, he would always call at her father's farm.

He was always sure of a good meal and a bed in the hay barn. In return, he used to saw firewood for kindling or sometimes he would chop logs .

It was an October morning when he arrived at our back door. How he found out where Anne lived after she got married, we never learned.

He was getting on in years by this time. Anne was happy to see him, but worried about him out in all weathers.

She gave him a meal, a bed in the barn and enough food, when he left, to keep him going for the rest of the week.

"Fleck, if you'd like to come on Christmas Day I'll give you a

Christmas dinner," she told him as he was leaving.

Well, on Christmas Day, Anne was just putting the vegetables on for dinner when there was a knock at the back door.

Who should be there but Fleck!

He had not only remembered Anne's promise, but also that it was Christmas Day.

Anne was delighted and asked him in, but he refused politely. He was happier out of doors, he said.

As dinner wasn't ready yet, I took him out a mug and a bottle of cider.

Later, Anne took him soup, a large plate of turkey and Christmas pudding.

I noticed she also took him some plastic bags in case he couldn't eat it all and wanted to save some for later.

He brought the plates back and gave Anne his thanks.

As he shuffled off across the yard, Anne shed a tear. She turned to me.

"John, how do we know that wasn't Jesus?" she said.

Well, I really didn't have the answer to that. ■

There's nowhere as beautiful as the countryside in the snow.

Published in Great Britain by D.C. Thomson & Co., Ltd., 185 Fleet Street, London EC4A 2HS

Tel. 01382 223 131
www.dcthomson.co.uk